LIFE SCIENCE LIBRARY

GROWTH

LIFE SCIENCE LIBRARY

CONSULTING EDITORS
René Dubos
Henry Margenau
C. P. Snow

GROWTH

by James M. Tanner, Gordon Rattray Taylor
and the Editors of **TIME-LIFE BOOKS**

TIME-LIFE BOOKS   NEW YORK

ABOUT THIS BOOK

THE COMPLEX, INTRICATE PROCESS of human growth is the subject of this book. An understanding of this process calls for insights from all the sciences concerned with man—from medicine to anthropology—and from experiments on insects, rats and apes. Text chapters and picture essays trace the timetable of human development from conception to maturity, describe the many patterns that growth displays and explore the frontiers of new research which may enable man to influence growth.

The alternating text chapters and picture essays can be read independently, although each essay supplements the chapter it follows. For example, Chapter 6, "Genes, Hormones and Environment," is followed by an essay which pictures in some detail the operation of the endocrine system, which manufactures the hormones that regulate growth.

THE AUTHORS

JAMES M. TANNER calls himself a "human biologist." He is an authority on physical growth and the development of learning ability and social behavior. An Englishman, he has an M.D. from Johns Hopkins Medical School and teaches at the University of London's Institute of Child Health. Author of many articles, he heads the Harpenden Growth Study, a childhood-to-maturity research project.

GORDON RATTRAY TAYLOR, a graduate of Trinity College, Cambridge, is a British writer noted for his popularization of science. Among his books are *Eye on Research* and a history of biology, *The Science of Life*. In addition, he edits a series of science programs for the BBC.

THE CONSULTING EDITORS

RENÉ DUBOS, a member and professor of The Rockefeller University, is a distinguished microbiologist and experimental pathologist who was awarded the Arches of Science Award in 1966. His books include *Mirage of Health* and *Man Adapting*. He is also coauthor of *Health and Disease* in this series.

HENRY MARGENAU is Eugene Higgins Professor of Physics and Natural Philosophy at Yale, and an authority in spectroscopy and nuclear physics. He wrote *Open Vistas, The Nature of Physical Reality*, and is coauthor of *The Scientist* in this series.

C. P. SNOW has won an international audience for his novels, including *The New Men, The Affair* and *Corridors of Power*, which explore the effects of science on today's society.

ON THE COVER

The small hand of a child rests on the palm of an adult, dramatizing the changes wrought in time by growth. On the back cover, symbols of amino acids and their linked sequence in a protein molecule represent the chemical synthesis that makes all growth possible.

Growth © 1965 Time Inc. All rights reserved. Revised 1969.
Published simultaneously in Canada. Library of Congress catalogue card number 65-26322.
School and library distribution by Silver Burdett Company, Morristown, New Jersey.

CONTENTS

TIME-LIFE BOOKS

EDITOR
Maitland A. Edey
EXECUTIVE EDITOR
Jerry Korn
TEXT DIRECTOR   ART DIRECTOR
Martin Mann   Sheldon Cotler
CHIEF OF RESEARCH
Beatrice T. Dobie
PICTURE EDITOR
Robert G. Mason
Assistant Text Directors:
Harold C. Field, Ogden Tanner
Assistant Art Director: Arnold C. Holeywell
Assistant Chief of Research: Martha T. Goolrick

PUBLISHER
Rhett Austell
Associate Publisher: Walter C. Rohrer
Assistant Publisher: Carter Smith
General Manager: Joseph C. Hazen Jr.
Business Manager: John D. McSweeney
Production Manager: Louis Bronzo

Sales Director: Joan D. Manley
Promotion Director: Beatrice K. Tolleris
Managing Director, International: John A. Millington

LIFE SCIENCE LIBRARY

SERIES EDITOR: Martin Mann
Editorial staff for *Growth:*
Associate Editor: Robert G. Mason
Text Editors: Nancy E. Gross, Alfred Lansing
Picture Editor: Wilbur L. Jarvis Jr.
Designer: Arnold C. Holeywell
Associate Designer: Edwin Taylor
Staff Writers: Timothy Carr, Peter M. Chaitin,
Jonathan Kastner, Harvey B. Loomis,
John Stanton
Chief Researcher: Thelma C. Stevens
Researchers: Sarah Bennett, Valentin Y. L. Chu,
Mollie Cooper, Leah Dunaief, Alice Kantor,
Robert R. McLaughlin, Marianna Pinchot,
Susanna Seymour, Rachel Tyrrell,
Victor H. Waldrop

EDITORIAL PRODUCTION
Color Director: Robert L. Young
Assistant: James J. Cox
Copy Staff: Rosalind Stubenberg,
Suzanne Seixas, Florence Keith
Picture Department: Dolores A. Littles,
Barbara Simon
Traffic: Arthur A. Goldberger
Art Assistants: Patricia Byrne,
Charles Mikolaycak

The text for the chapters of this book was written by James M. Tanner and Gordon Rattray Taylor, for the picture essays by the editorial staff. The following individuals and departments of Time Inc. were helpful in the production of the book: LIFE Staff photographer Bill Ray; Editorial Production, Robert W. Boyd Jr.; Editorial Reference, Peter Draz; Picture Collection, Doris O'Neil; Photographic Laboratory, George Karas; TIME-LIFE News Service, Richard M. Clurman.

INTRODUCTION

THERE IS NO MORE FASCINATING STUDY in life than investigation of life itself. The perpetuation of living organisms involves the processes of growth and development, which are the subjects of this small volume. Much is known about the forces that stimulate and control growth but there are many challenging areas for future investigation. What are the forces that initiate the specialization of cells in the developing organism and result in the appearance of new, multiple and varied functions? What are the mechanisms that control growth, and why does it sometimes go astray? These and other important questions are discussed in this book in an interesting and readable manner. Both the known and unknown, the intriguing unsolved problems, are given consideration.

Potentialities for growth are inherent at the time of conception and are determined by the genes—the carriers of heredity—but without a favorable environment, normal growth cannot occur. There are many environmental factors that influence growth, an adequate supply of proper nutrients being of greatest importance. Nutrients are the chemical substances in foods that must be used by the cell to reduplicate itself, to specialize and to carry out its prescribed functions. While the achievement of optimal growth is determined in large part by the child's genetic makeup, the environment into which he is born markedly influences his future course.

After conception, when fusion of the male and female cell occurs, nutrition is furnished by the egg cell prior to implantation in the uterus. Then, the developing embryo obtains its nourishment from the body of the mother. The mother's nutrition is of great importance in furnishing the nutrients demanded by the growing fetus.

After the child is born, nutrients must be supplied in the form of food. The quantities of nutrients needed are determined by the rate of growth and development. They are great in proportion to body size in the first year of life when growth is rapid, decrease for the next few years and increase again markedly during the adolescent growth spurt.

The factual material presented in the several chapters of this book is scientifically accurate and chosen from a wide vista of biological knowledge. In addition to discussing biological aspects of growth in various animal species and man, some of the social, cultural and psychological aspects of human growth are considered, particularly in the chapter on adolescence. The measurement and evaluation of growth are discussed, and the role of various environmental factors that influence growth are given consideration. The intellectually curious will find satisfaction and stimulation in this book.

—GRACE A. GOLDSMITH, M.D.
Chairman, Food and Nutrition Board
National Academy of Sciences—National Research Council

1
A 20th Century Challenge

JOURNEY TOWARD ADULTHOOD
Approaching the swiftest years of growth, pre-adolescent playmates frolic on a Saturn-shaped jungle gym in a Los Angeles park. The period that lies close ahead of them is not only a time of tremendously swift increase in size but also years during which a bewildering departure is made from childhood and a start begun on the momentous journey toward adulthood.

OF ALL THE CHALLENGES that confront 20th Century biology, the study of growth is among the greatest and the most exciting. The process meets the eye at every turn. Plants sprout, eggs hatch, and the overalls that fit four-year-old Johnnie in the spring are up above his ankles by winter. But these events, far from being commonplace, are a continual wonder to behold, and many of them still mystify scientists.

Growth is an extraordinarily complicated business, at least in living things. In the realm of inanimate matter, it is relatively easy to understand. There it consists of an increase in size: crystals grow, for example, and so do icicles and stalactites and stalagmites. But the mechanisms of their enlargement are very different from those that make organic growth possible. The inanimate object grows from the outside, by simple accretion. It merely adds onto its surface more and more of the material of which it is composed. The living organism, on the other hand, grows by metabolism, from within. It takes in all kinds of substances, breaks them down into their chemical components to provide energy and then reassembles them into new materials. Living things, no matter what their specific natures, have to work to grow. This is as true of the single-celled amoeba as it is of man.

In addition to increase in size, organic growth involves differentiation and change in form. The oak tree bears no more resemblance to the acorn from which it sprang than a baby does to the fertilized egg. Living things become more complex as they grow. They acquire specialized parts that they did not have to begin with and arrange these parts in a more elaborate way.

The three elements—increase in size, differentiation of structure and alteration of form—constitute something more than simple growth. Together, they comprise development, the series of orderly and irreversible stages that every organism goes through from the beginning of its life to the end. In everyday speech, the words "growth" and "development" are used almost interchangeably. To the scientist, however, growth is only one aspect of the larger process of development.

No two living organisms are exactly alike. Each grows and develops in a unique fashion within the limits that its environment permits. Every species, however, has its own way of growing, and each has its own rate of growth. The range of variations is overwhelming. In as little as three months, for example, one of the grasses native to tropical Ceylon, a bamboo, may shoot up to a height of 120 feet, as tall as a 12-story building, by growing at an average rate of 16 inches a day. A eucalyptus native to Uganda has been known to grow 45 feet in two years, whereas dwarf ivy generally grows only one inch a year. The majestic sequoia of California, which starts out as a seed weighing only one three-thousandth of an ounce, may end up 270 feet tall, with a base diameter of 40 feet and a weight estimated at 6,200 tons. It takes more than 1,000 years for the sequoia to achieve the feat of multiplying 600 billion times in mass.

The animal kingdom, too, has its champions of growth. The blue whale, which cruises the oceans from the North to the South Pole, begins life as a barely visible egg weighing only a fraction of an ounce. At birth, it weighs from two to three tons. When it is weaned, at about seven months, it is 52 feet long and weighs 23 tons, having gained an average of 200 pounds a day. By the time it reaches maturity, in about 13 years, the blue whale is serious competition for many submarines. Then it may weigh more than 85 tons and exceed 80 feet in length.

Facts and figures of growth, however, are far less interesting to the scientist than the investigation of the many processes involved in growth and development. It is the multiplicity of these processes, the intricacy of some of them, and the recurrence of many of them in all kinds of different things that attract his attention. For example: tapeworms, human hair and animal fur all lengthen according to a similar scheme. Their growth is initiated from one major point. The tapeworm's body develops from front to back, starting from a spot just behind its head. Fur and hair grow from one point, the root. Plants, on the other hand, have at least two growing points, one just behind the tip of the root, the other just behind the tip of the stem.

Sometimes growth proceeds in many directions at once, and at different rates in different parts of the same structure. The inner ear, which transmits aural messages to the brain, begins as nothing more than a thickened mass of tissue in the embryo. In a brief six weeks, by a complex pattern of differential growth, it transforms itself into a closed sphere and then into an elaborate, labyrinthine system of fluid-filled chambers and canals.

Geometry in growth

Rigid objects show another pattern of growth. The shells of marine animals increase in width as well as length, retaining their shapes all the while. Shells are rigid, and cannot be stretched or twisted. How nature solves the problem of retaining shape while expanding size can be seen in a clam shell. The material between any two of the crescent-like lines across its width is one growth unit. Each of these gnomons, as they are called, is a trifle larger in all its dimensions than the one that preceded it. Gnomons permit objects to increase in size without changing in form. They are the growth units for many kinds of rigid things, including marine shells, horns and tusks.

Not all rigid objects grow by the addition of gnomons. If the proportions of the long bones of the body are not to be radically altered as they grow, the diameters of their marrow-filled cavities must increase at the same time that the bones as a whole widen. This kind of growth requires destruction as well as construction. As new deposits are laid down on the outer surface of the growing bone, old ones are destroyed on its inner surface. One group of cells, the osteoclasts, destroys the old bone while another group, the osteoblasts, is building the new.

Cells: the fundamental unit

Bone, shells and nails are essentially secretions, like tears and sweat. They are among the metabolic products of the cells. It is the cells that are the fundamental units of life, and it is in them that the basic mysteries of growth and development are hidden.

All cells are tiny blobs of the kind of matter known as protoplasm. All are made on the same basic plan. They have an outer wall, the cell membrane, within which resides the body of the cell, the cytoplasm. In the cytoplasm is the nucleus. The cell functions as a whole, so that all its parts interact with one another. However, each part specializes in function. The membrane determines which materials from outside can enter the body of the cell. The cytoplasm is primarily a manufacturing plant. Here, various specialized structures do the work of converting material from the environment into usable form. And the nucleus, through the chromosomes and genes that it contains, is the control center for all the processes of growth and development.

The body of the average adult human being contains 60 trillion cells. All have developed from a single fertilized egg. To produce this fantastic increase in number, individual cells must divide over and over, creating daughter cells that are identical with one another and with their parent. Each daughter cell contains half the mass of the parent. But the chromosomes inside the nucleus have not been divided in half. At some point before the cell divided, the chromosomes began reproducing themselves. After division occurred, each daughter cell contained precisely the same number and kind of chromosomes as did the parent.

The process by which this extraordinary event occurs can be seen by examining a stained section of a living plant under a special type of microscope. As the cell prepares to split, the chromosomes, which were originally distributed widely through the nucleus, begin to coil up and to appear as separate threads. When all the threads have become distinct, each one separates into two. Then one set of chromosomes migrates to one end of the cell, another to the opposite end. Each set establishes itself within a nucleus, and a new cell membrane appears in the middle of the old cell. When the cell divides, a full set of chromosomes is available for each of the daughter cells.

The chromosomes contain nearly all the information needed to construct a complete organism. Every form of life has its own number of

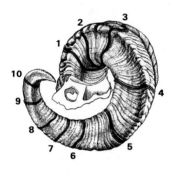

ANNUAL GROWTH RINGS occur in the horn of a ram *(above)* in much the same way as they do in a tree trunk *(below)*. The number of rings that form indicate the age of the organism, while the size of any one ring reflects its growth rate during a particular year. For its species, the 11-year-old ram, whose horn is shown, grew at a normal rate. The 42-year-old tree, however, began life in an unfavorable environment, and so developed slowly at first in its rise to maturity.

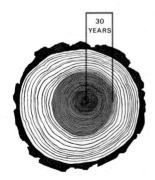

chromosomes. The lowly fruit fly has eight, the human being 46. Science has known of the existence of the chromosomes since the end of the 19th Century, but it was not until the 1940s that biochemists began to discover the chemical composition of their genetic material, a substance called deoxyribonucleic acid, or DNA. By 1953 the chemical composition of DNA had been established, and in that same year James D. Watson and F.H.C. Crick were able to create a model revealing its structure. Their work, which earned them a Nobel Prize in 1962, showed this fundamental material of life, the chemical basis of heredity, to be a long, twisted molecule, consisting of four repeating subunits which are arranged in a different order in each molecule. The order of these units determines the physical characteristics of the organism containing them.

The processes by which cells grow are reflected in the patterns of growth of the larger structures, such as tissues and organs, that they make up. In some of these structures, the cycle of cellular growth and reproduction continues throughout life, although it proceeds at a particularly rapid pace during the early years. An adult has more skin cells than a baby, and more blood cells too. In contrast with the structures that grow by increasing their total number of cells, others grow after their initial formation only by increasing the size and complexity of their cells. This is the pattern of growth followed by the most specialized organs of the human body. The heart of a newborn baby boy is only one sixteenth as large as the heart of a grown man, but it contains exactly the same number of cells. The same thing is true of the brain. Before birth, every individual has a full complement of nerve cells. With growth, the cells become larger, developing the extensions, axons and dendrites, which interconnect nerve cells. As time goes on, the axons and dendrites become longer, and their interconnections more complex.

Sometimes growth begins again, in response to need, long after it would normally have stopped. When disease requires the removal of one of the two adrenal glands, the other enlarges to compensate for the loss. Similarly, if the heart pumps against abnormal pressure, as it has to in a person who suffers from hypertension, the added work will stimulate an increase in its size and strength. This kind of growth is not always associated with disease. An athlete's muscles are better developed than those of a sedentary worker.

From flower to fruit

In many forms of life, from plants to man, increases in size and complexity are accompanied by spectacular changes in form. An apple begins as a blossom. Near the base of the flower is the ovary containing ovules, the precursors of seeds. As the blossom transforms itself into a fruit, the skin of the ovule becomes the hard coat of the pip. At the

A MOMENTOUS MASTERPIECE, William Harvey's *De generatione animalium* helped launch embryology as a science with its painstakingly accurate descriptions of the stages in the development of the chick embryo. This title page from the first edition of 1651 shows Zeus freeing animals from an egg which bears the inscription "Ex ovo omnia," Harvey's famous, but not entirely accurate, belief that "everything comes from the egg."

same time, the ovary and other nearby sections of the flower expand enormously, by cell division, until they become the flesh of the apple. The petals die and fall away.

Equally spectacular are the processes which transform a fertilized egg into a baby, the baby into a child, an adolescent, and finally an adult. The changes that occur in the womb are, of course, the most extraordinary, and the forces that lie behind them are still only partly understood. What stimulates a cell to divide? What starts cell specialization? How do these blobs of matter learn to differentiate, to have different forms and to perform different functions? What are the forces that impel similar cells to come together to form tissues and organs? What sets the timetable for the emergence of structures and functions in the embryo? And what can happen in those nine precarious months to upset the delicate balance and cause a distortion of development? What governs the growth of the child after he is born? Why does he grow proportionately more in the first year of his life than in the sixth? Why does his head reach its full size more quickly than his feet? Why do 20th Century girls reach puberty earlier than those of the 19th?

Some elemental questions

What are the roles that heredity and environment play in directing growth? And how do they work together with those major body chemicals, the hormones, to determine the child's differing rates of growth at different times of life? How are the changes galvanized that take place at puberty? What turns a boy into a man, and a girl into a young woman?

These are some of the questions that science has been asking and investigating, and their answers make up part of this book. Not all of the basic questions can be answered with full confidence, but science is pushing ahead anyway to experiment in much more esoteric and possibly fateful areas. Some of the work being done with animals may sound to many laymen like out-and-out science fiction. Experiments have already produced some fairly bizarre results. Embryologists have created newts that are Siamese twins with two heads and a single body. Entomologists have extended the larval stage in certain insects far beyond its normal span, and have kept the creatures growing all the while. They have, in other words, prolonged youth. Zoologists have made it possible for inferior strains of livestock to give birth to purebred offspring. Psychologists have derailed normal behavioral growth and development in monkeys and have then set it back on the track.

One day it may be possible to apply this kind of new knowledge for the benefit of man. Then it may be possible to control human growth, not to breed a race of supermen, but to guarantee that every child is born healthy, and has the opportunity to achieve his maximum potential.

FOLLOWING HARVEY, William Langly published in 1674 his studies on the growing chick embryo. Unlike Harvey's *De generatione*, Langly's work was illustrated with carefully executed drawings like these, which show the rapid changes that occur in the first three days of the chick's embryonic development.

NEW-LAID EGG

BLOOD VESSELS FORMING

ENLARGING EMBRYO

At present, these opportunities are determined in very large part by his parents. The environment into which they bring him sharply influences the future course of his growth, and his heredity plays a large part in determining the characteristics he will have. Much of his future is established at the very moment sperm and egg unite. A number of physical characteristics are set at this time: sex; eye color; color and quality of hair; blood type. At conception he may also be doomed to disease. All of these characteristics are set by the genes contained in the chromosomes. The single cell that represents the first stage of human development is itself produced by the fusion of two cells. From the father comes the sperm, one of billions continually being mass-produced in the testes. From the mother comes the egg, one of which is normally released every month from the ovaries. These two kinds of cells are different from each other, and different, too, from all the other cells in the human body.

The seeds of life

The sperm is the active member of the pair; it has to travel to meet the egg, and it is admirably constructed for this job. The human sperm is a stripped-down cell, shaped something like a tadpole. The oval head, the heaviest part of the cell, contains very little cytoplasm. It is composed primarily of chromosomes tightly packed together. Behind the head is the small midpiece, or body, filled with structures called mitochondria. The mitochondria are power units, which are found in many kinds of cells. They are, however, particularly abundant in the sperm, which needs considerable energy to travel its course. At the end of the sperm is a long, thin tail which whips from side to side to propel the cell. The sperm's streamlined shape and its economy of structure permit it to move at a relatively rapid rate. It travels at an average speed of an estimated one tenth of an inch per minute, no small feat for a cell so light and tiny that 100,000 of them tightly packed together would still be barely visible. The sperm are manufactured in almost astronomical quantity. It has been estimated that from 300 million to 500 million are released to meet each egg.

Compared to the sperm, the egg is enormous. It is one of the largest cells in the body, so large that it is visible to the naked eye. Although it weighs only a millionth of a gram, it contains a considerable amount of cytoplasm, as well as a small amount of yolk used to nourish the fertilized egg in its earliest stages. The ovaries contain an estimated 400,000 eggs, of which from 300 to 400 are released during a woman's fertile years.

When sperm and egg fuse, the father's contribution to his offspring is primarily in the genetic material contained in the head of the sperm.

THE PROCESS OF FERTILIZATION is traced in the diagrams below. It begins when a sperm wiggles its way into the egg (1) and contributes a body, the centrosome, to the cytoplasm (2). The centrosome migrates to the egg's center, where it divides to form the spindle (3). There, the male and female nuclei, each carrying half the chromosomes needed to determine the baby's genetic makeup, fuse (4). The chromosomes then line up and divide to create two daughter cells (5, 6 and 7). The whole process (from 1 through 7) takes about 36 hours.

(1) SPERM PENETRATES EGG

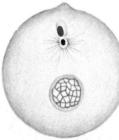

(2) CENTROSOME APPEARS

(3) SPINDLE FORMS

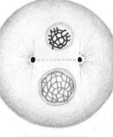

(4) NUCLEI JOIN

And it is this contribution that determines the infant's sex. All the cells of the human body, except the sperm and the egg, contain 46 chromosomes, arranged in the nucleus in 23 pairs. One of these pairs is associated with the individual's sex. In women, the members of this pair are identical with each other, both being the so-called X chromosome. In men, however, the members of this pair are not identical. Male cells have one X chromosome and one of a very different type, known as Y.

Not only is there a difference in the chromosomal composition of men's and women's body cells, but the sperm and the egg are different in their chromosomal numbers from all the other cells in the body. The sperm and the egg contain only 23 chromosomes apiece—one member of each pair. This reduction in number, a necessity if the fertilized egg is to have only 46 chromosomes, is accomplished by a special form of cell division called meiosis. Since the precursor cell from which the eggs develop contained two X chromosomes, every egg contains one X chromosome. But the sperm precursors contain one X and one Y. When meiosis occurs, each newly formed sperm may therefore contain either an X or a Y chromosome. Chance seems to determine which members of the chromosome pairs meiosis will give to any egg or sperm—in other words, which of a parent's characteristics the child will inherit. This explains the often startling differences among offspring of the same parents. Chance also seems to determine whether the sperm that finally penetrates the egg is one that carries an X or a Y chromosome. But once the penetration is accomplished, there is no more room for chance. If the chromosome is an X, a female has been conceived. If it is a Y, a male has been conceived.

The parents' equal roles

The facts that the father determines the sex of his child and that both parents contribute equally to its inheritance were not always appreciated. Aristotle recognized that both play a role, but his interpretation of those roles was entirely incorrect. He believed that the embryo developed from a "coagulum" of menstrual fluid; the mother supplied the material, the father the form. But many of his contemporaries disagreed with his view. They held that the father played the only active role. He sowed the seed, and the woman provided the fertile ground in which it was nourished. As the Greek playwright Aeschylus wrote, in the *Eumenides:* "The mother of what is called her child is no parent of it, but nurse only of the young life that is sown in her." In the 18th Century, when embryology was still in its infancy, opinion was sharply divided between the spermists and the ovists, between those who believed, with the ancients, that the father was the child's only true parent and those who believed that the mother was, with the corol-

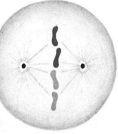

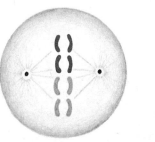

(5) CHROMOSOMES LINE UP   (6) CHROMOSOMES DIVIDE   (7) DAUGHTER CELLS SEPARATE

lary that the father's role was merely to stimulate the growth process.

Although both exclusive viewpoints had been abandoned by the early 19th Century, it was not until 1944 that the Harvard University gynecologist John Rock, who later helped develop the birth-control pill, actually witnessed the fertilization of a human egg. Dr. Rock and his assistant, Miriam F. Menkin, took a human egg that had been surgically removed from a woman's ovary and put it in a small dish. Then they put in some live male sperm. After letting the mixture stand for an hour at room temperature, they placed it in a culture of human blood serum. In 40 hours, the single fertilized egg had split into two cells.

It is difficult to tell how long the actual process of fertilization takes, from the moment the sperm begin to make their way up to the uterus to the moment one of them unites with the egg. Experiments indicate, however, that the time lapse is no longer than an hour.

Science does not know as yet what the properties are that permit one particular sperm among all the millions finally to succeed, and to make an entry into the egg. It does know, however, that once this entry is accomplished, the nuclei of sperm and egg unite into one. At that moment the fertilization process is completed. And then there begins the long sequence of complex events which, if all goes well, will result nine months later in the birth of a baby.

The Manufacture
of
Building Blocks

The key to growth is the production of protein molecules. During its long journey to maturity, the human body must produce billions of new cells for its growing tissues, muscles and organs. The new cells, in turn, are made of new molecules. A majority of the molecules are proteins, substances whose name is derived from a Greek word meaning "holding first place." Apart from water, proteins are the most important group of compounds in the body, accounting for three quarters of its dry weight. Because each species of plant and animal possesses its own unique set of proteins, man cannot utilize directly the proteins he consumes in animal or plant foods. Instead, his body must act as a chemical factory, transforming the food into a set of proteins made to his own measure. This process is growth at its most fundamental level, for without the steady mass production of new molecules, none of the other processes of growth could take place.

WHAT THE CELL NEEDS

As shown on the opposite page, three classes of chemical substances are involved in the growth of cells and thereby the growth of human beings. Nutrients from outside the body—foods, water and oxygen—supply raw materials for cell growth, which is the basis for the growth of the body. Genes direct the processing of the materials; hormones speed the processing and stimulate genes.

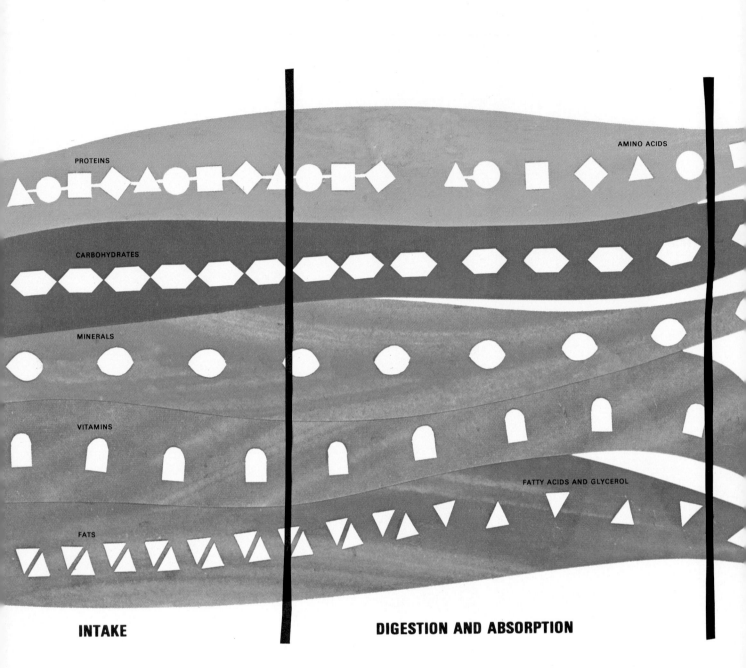

PROTEINS

AMINO ACIDS

CARBOHYDRATES

MINERALS

VITAMINS

FATTY ACIDS AND GLYCEROL

FATS

INTAKE

DIGESTION AND ABSORPTION

The First Step: Raw Materials

Five kinds of chemicals from food, along with water and oxygen, constitute the raw materials for growth. Of these foodstuffs, two—vitamins and minerals—come ready for immediate use. The other three must be chemically broken down into simpler substances before individual cells can admit and utilize them. Until this process has been carried out, these nutrients are as useless to the cell as a whole tree would be to a carpen-

ter. Digestion, starting in the mouth but taking place chiefly in the stomach and small intestine, accomplishes this necessary transformation of large nutrients into acceptably small units. Proteins are split into amino acids (there are 23 kinds), carbohydrates into simple sugars, fats into fatty acids and glycerol. From the digestive sites in the alimentary canal, the processed chemicals, as well as the unprocessed vitamins and min-

BLOOD

CELL

LYMPH

CIRCULATION

FOOD ROUTES TO THE CELL

After digestion, the five food chemicals needed for growth are delivered to the cell *(above)* through two circulatory systems: the bloodstream and the lymphatic system. Blood transports water-soluble nutrients. The lymph, a fluid derived chiefly from blood plasma, carries most fats plus nutrients that dissolve only in fats.

erals, are absorbed into the bloodstream or the lymph and carried to the cells. There, the amino acids, fatty acids, glycerol and minerals will be assembled into new compounds that will form structural components such as cell membrane. The sugars will be used mostly to supply energy for the assembly process. The vitamins will serve as chemical expediters, or catalysts, which will speed the synthesis of the new compounds.

PROCESSING SITES IN A CELL

This partial view of a human cell, magnified 27,000 times in an electron micrograph, shows the four basic components that maintain cell life and growth. (Components labeled above are described in the captions on the opposite page.) The cell, taken from a human salivary gland, manufactures proteins of the sort called enzymes. These particular enzymes begin to split carbohydrates such as starch into sugars.

A
NUCLEAR PATTERNS FOR GROWTH

The nucleus contains genetic "blueprints" that supply the patterns *(symbolized at right)* that govern the cell's assembly of proteins—each kind differently patterned—and other molecules.

B
ACTIVE CELL WALL

The cell wall permits some chemicals to seep directly through it, but must actively assist others, such as amino acids. These are conveyed into the cell by "carrier" molecules *(right)*.

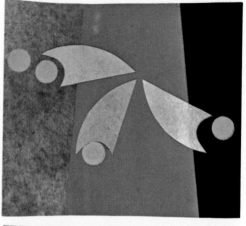

C
MITOCHONDRIAL POWER PLANT

Within the mitochondria, sugars are broken down, releasing energy *(right)*. Packed into storage molecules, this energy will then serve to power growth and all other cellular processes.

D
THE SYNTHESIZING RIBOSOMES

Throughout the cell, ribosomes, using power stored by the mitochondria and acting under nuclear instructions, link separate amino acids into the long chains that are proteins *(right)*.

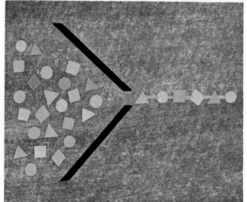

A Microscopic Chemical Factory

The chemical synthesis on which all growth depends takes place in the cell, a body only a thousandth of an inch in diameter. A microminiature chemical plant, the cell is enclosed by a membrane about a third of a millionth of an inch thick. This membrane serves less as a wall than as a living filter that accepts certain substances and excludes others. When necessary, it can boost molecules in from the blood and lymph. Within the cell, sausage-shaped particles called mitochondria generate, store and supply energy on demand. Depending upon its specific function, a cell may have from 50 to 5,000 of these power plants. High-production cells, such as those found in the pancreas, have an especially large complement of mitochondria. The actual work of synthesis—assembling amino acids into proteins—is done by the ribosomes, microscopic spheres half a millionth of an inch in diameter, using power from the mitochondria. Ribosomes are found all through the cell sap, or cytoplasm, usually attached to membranes called the endoplasmic reticulum. Directing all the cell's activities is the nucleus. Enclosed in a porous membrane of its own, the nucleus dictates the particular form of the various kinds of protein that the cell manufactures.

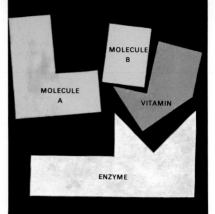

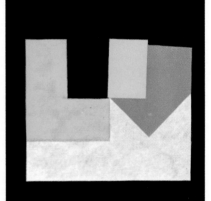

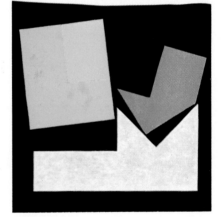

MEETING, JOINING, LEAVING

In the drawings above, an enzyme and a vitamin act as efficient chemical matchmakers, marrying two separate molecules, A and B, into a new compound. The enzyme serves as the one and only common meeting place where this union can occur. A vitamin, acting as temporary escort to molecule B *(top)*, is chemically attracted and exactly fitted to a particular site on the enzyme surface. Meanwhile, molecule A drops into an adjacent slot on the enzyme *(middle)*. Brought close together, molecules A and B now are so strongly attracted to each other that they quickly merge to form a new substance *(bottom)*. As they leave together, the enzyme and the vitamin break apart, preparing themselves to perform their matchmaking task all over again.

The Body's Vital Expediters

For living things to maintain themselves and grow, chemical reactions have to be carried out rapidly. The speedup is performed by chemical expediting agents called catalysts. With the aid of catalysts, cells can accomplish in seconds changes that would otherwise require days or even centuries. The human body employs four kinds of catalysts: enzymes, hormones, minerals and vitamins, but enzymes are by far the most important. Of the body's thousands of different chemical reactions, every one is expedited by a specific enzyme. Assisting the enzymes are approximately 20 minerals, vitamins and hormones. Enzymes are at work all through the process by which ingested food is transformed into new protein. In the digestive tract, they help to convert foodstuffs into compounds that cells can utilize. Enzymes within the cell membrane help to transport nutrients through it. In the mitochondria, enzymes preside over each step of the intricate process by which sugars are broken down to yield energy. Finally, enzymes play a critical role in the protein assembly line, attracting, clasping and joining small molecules to construct bigger ones *(left)*. Enzymes themselves are proteins—chains of from 124 to 10,000 or more linked amino acids. Thus, enzymes help produce more of themselves, as well as everything that the cell manufactures.

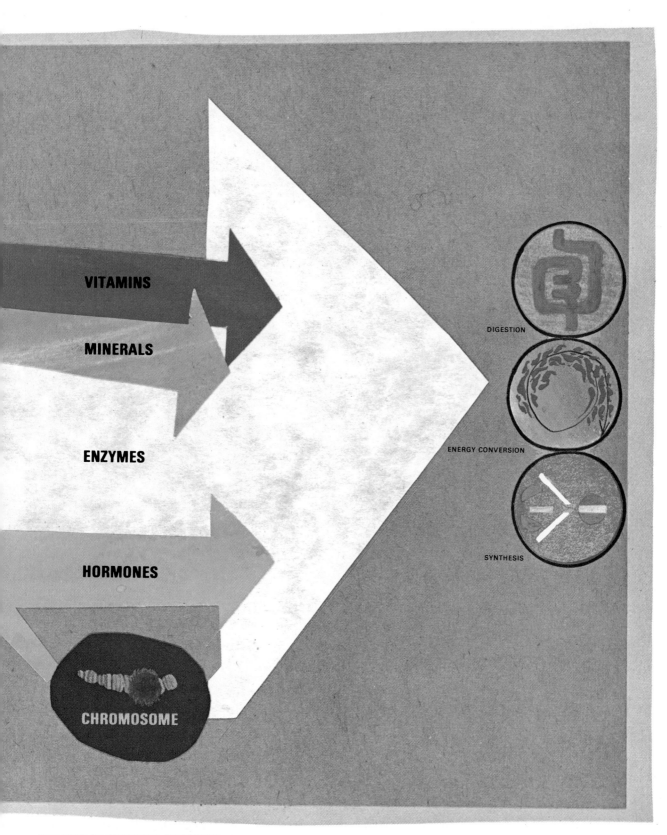

DIGESTION

ENERGY CONVERSION

SYNTHESIS

VITAMINS

MINERALS

ENZYMES

HORMONES

CHROMOSOME

QUARTET OF CHEMICAL BOOSTERS
Four catalytic agents speed virtually all life and growth processes. The enzymes, preeminent among these catalysts, sometimes act on their own to quicken such processes as digestion, energy conversion and synthesis *(above, right)*. More often, however, they are assisted by "cofactors": vitamins, minerals or hormones. The hormones also play an independent role, stimulating portions of the chromosomes, the bearers of the cell's hereditary "blueprints." In some animals, a bit of chromosome may respond visibly to the stimulus by puffing up *(bottom, center)*.

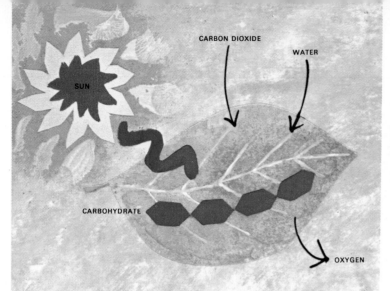

CARBON DIOXIDE

WATER

SUN

CARBOHYDRATE

OXYGEN

ENERGY PACKAGED BY PLANTS
Through photosynthesis, plants *(left)* convert the energy of sunlight into a form accessible to man. The energy serves to join carbon dioxide from the air with water from the earth, reassembling their atoms into carbohydrates, energy-containing chains of sugar molecules. Oxygen is given off as waste during the process.

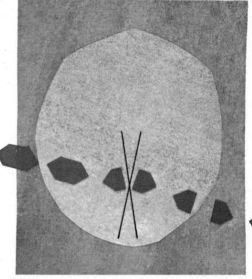

CARBOHYDRATE

BREAKING THE PACKET DOWN
In the digestive tract, carbohydrate molecular chains formed by plants are broken up by enzymes into simple sugars, chiefly glucose, that can then be directly utilized by individual cells.

SPLITTING UP THE FUEL
Within the cell, glucose molecules are snipped in two *(above)* in a process known as glycolysis. Each of the dozen steps in this process of division is catalyzed by a specific enzyme.

Power for the Protein Factory

Protein synthesis, like every other manufacturing process, requires energy. This energy, like nearly all the forms of energy utilized by man, ultimately derives from the sun. Solar energy, incorporated into chemical compounds by plants, comes to man in the form of plant foods or the meat of plant-eating animals. But these substances, unmodified, are useless to the cell. Like coal shipped to a factory powerhouse, the fuel molecules must be "burned" so that their energy can be converted into a usable form. In this process, food energy is transferred to the compound adenosine triphosphate (ATP), the universal currency of cellular energy transactions. The conversion takes place through a complex sequence of reactions called the Krebs cycle, after its discoverer, Sir Hans Krebs, who won a Nobel Prize for his discovery. The cycle, which "burns" food as a power plant burns coal, harnesses about two thirds of the food energy, an efficiency almost double that of the newest man-made power plants.

ENERGY-CONVERSION CYCLE

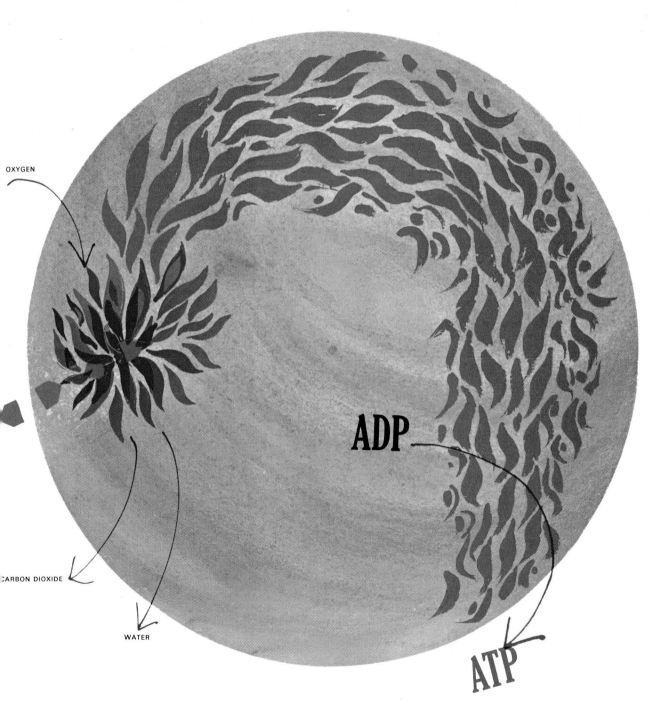

OXYGEN

CARBON DIOXIDE

WATER

ADP

ATP

ENERGY CONVERTED FOR USE

Within the mitochondrion, split glucose molecules are "burned" as fuel in the Krebs cycle *(above)*, which reverses the process of photosynthesis. In photosynthesis, carbon dioxide plus water plus energy yield carbohydrates plus oxygen; in the Krebs cycle, carbohydrates plus oxygen yield carbon dioxide, water and energy. The energy converts molecules of adenosine diphosphate (ADP) into adenosine triphosphate (ATP). During the Krebs cycle, which includes some 20 stages, energy from one molecule of glucose is used to form 36 molecules of ATP.

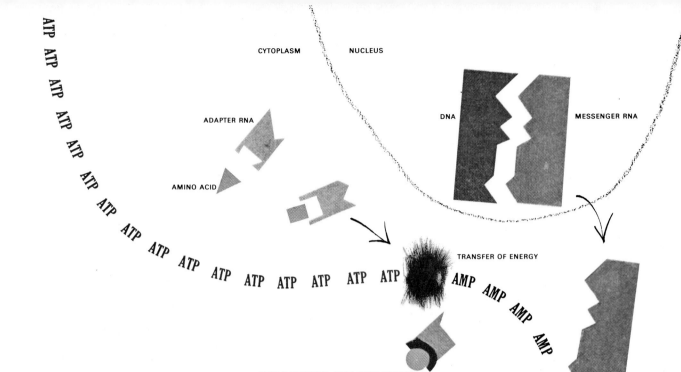

CYTOPLASM NUCLEUS

ADAPTER RNA

AMINO ACID

DNA MESSENGER RNA

ATP ATP ATP ATP ATP ATP ATP ATP ATP ATP ATP ATP ATP ATP ATP ATP ATP

TRANSFER OF ENERGY

AMP AMP AMP AMP

THE PATTERN AND THE PIECES

Protein synthesis begins in the cell nucleus *(above, right)*, where the compound DNA imposes its chemical pattern on another substance, RNA. This serves as a messenger to carry the pattern outside the nucleus. Meanwhile, amino acids have been linked to patterned "adapters"—smaller molecules of RNA—by energy from ATP, leaving behind adenosine monophosphate (AMP). The "adapted" amino acids and messenger RNA move to the ribosome.

RIBOSOME

THE ASSEMBLY LINE IN ACTION

On the ribosome *(right)*, adapter RNAs lock into the patterned structure of messenger RNA. The energy that first served to bind the amino acid to the adapter RNA now shifts to bind succeeding amino acids to one another. The resulting chain of amino acids *(below, right)* is a protein.

PROTEIN

Turning Out the End Product

A protein is like a long string of beads, with each bead being one of 23 amino acids; the sequence of amino acids determines the protein's specific properties and thus its function. The stringing together of amino acids into proteins, in sequences determined by the cell nucleus, as diagramed on this page, is the key chemical step in the growth process.

The body produces a prodigious variety of proteins, which serve it in all sorts of capacities. Structurally, they are the major components of hair, skin, muscle, blood vessels and internal organs. Functionally, they supply enzymes, the blood's hemoglobin and some hormones, such as insulin. From birth to age 20, a human being synthesizes an estimated 500 to 1,000 pounds of protein, but nearly all of this enormous quantity is required to replace aged or damaged cells. The net buildup in body protein is a very modest 20 to 40 pounds. In muscle, protein makes up 80 per cent of the nonwater weight; in blood, 90 per cent. Even in bone, the dry weight is 35 per cent protein.

PROTEINS BY THE THOUSAND

The diversity of body proteins is suggested by the permutations of symbols in the painting opposite; each symbol represents an amino acid. Many thousands of different proteins are required in the body. The smallest contains 50 amino acids, others contain tens of thousands.

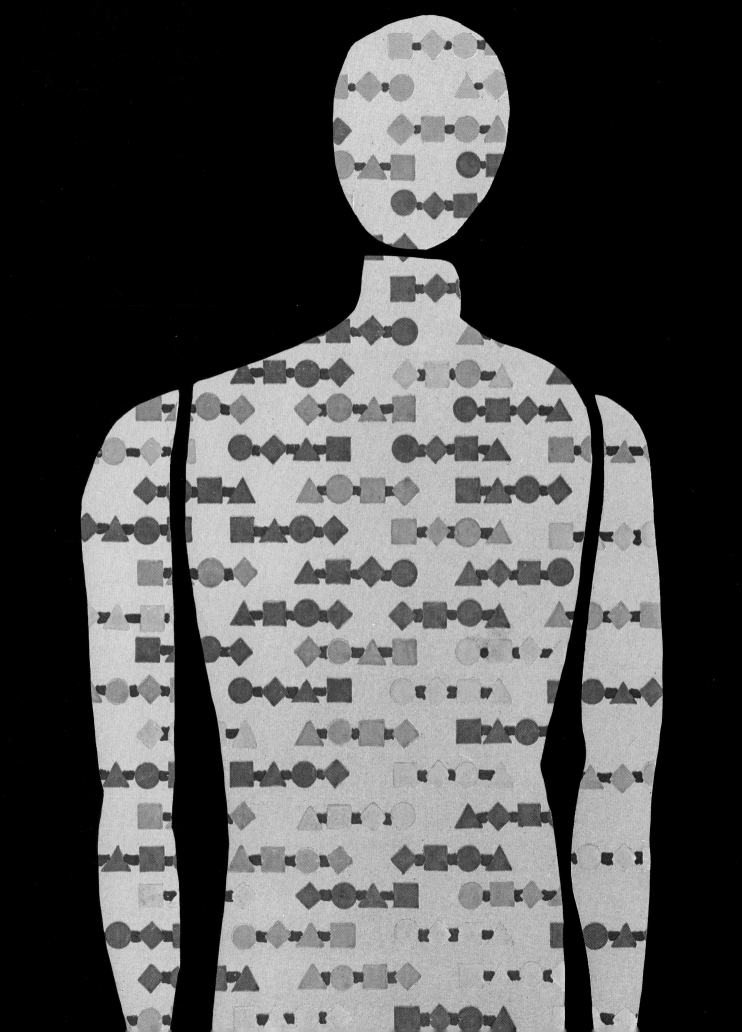

2

The First
Two Months

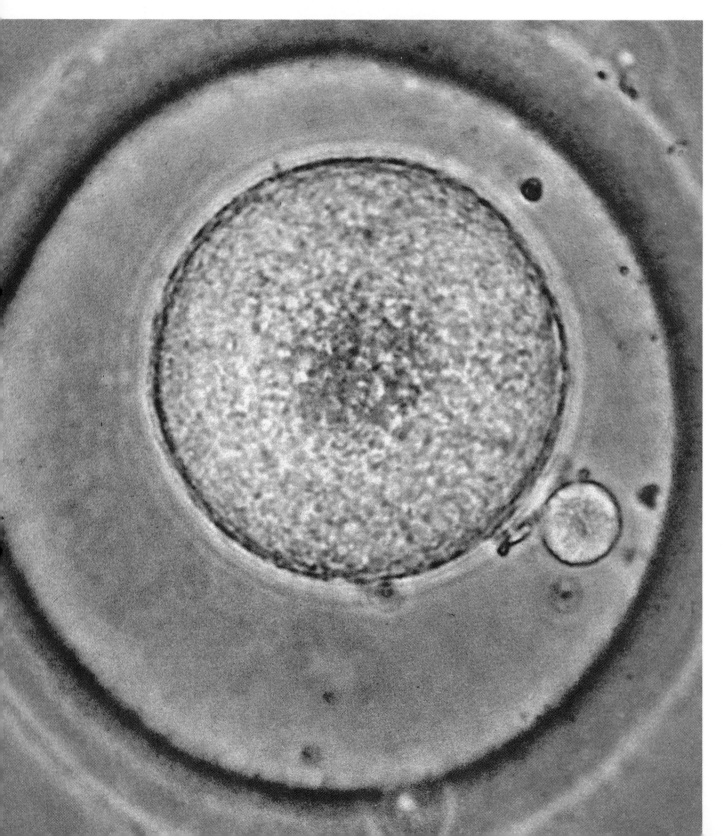

THE PARENTS of a strapping teen-age son may find it hard to remember that their offspring was once a tiny seven-pounder. In less than a score of years, he has increased in height about three and a half times and in weight more than 20 times, at the same time changing from an infant to a man. But this visible growth and transformation are infinitesimal compared with those that take place in the first two months he spends in his mother's womb. There, in eight brief weeks, he increases in length about 240 times and in weight one million times; he grows from a single fertilized egg into a miniature baby.

From his mother's body he absorbs the raw materials with which he builds the structures needed for life. Elaborate and little-understood mechanisms guard the delicate embryo against harm—even from its own mother. The startling fact is that normal processes of the mother's body should seemingly abort every developing baby. Biologists are still trying to discover why abortions are not the rule rather than the exception. Other researchers are working out the details of how the growing embryo develops, guided by submicroscopic "blueprints" in its cells and further shaped by still-obscure interactions among its own parts. Human growth and development are, from the very beginning, rigorously patterned and controlled.

First come the more vital necessities. The most obvious of these is a nutritional system to supply the embryo with the raw materials for growth. This need the mother's body regularly anticipates. Every month the wall of the uterus grows a thick, spongy lining, rich in blood vessels. If the egg that has been released during this period is not fertilized by a sperm, the lining is sloughed off in menstruation. But if conception occurs, the lining remains and grows thicker, readying itself to receive the embryo and to supply it with nutrients from the mother's body.

The sperm and egg unite in one of the Fallopian tubes, the ducts that lead from the ovaries to the womb. The fertilized egg takes three or four days to drift down into its future home, dividing steadily all the time. By the time it arrives in the uterus, it has grown to a spherical cluster of several dozen cells. In the uterus it floats about for a few more days, continuing to divide. At the same time, its structure changes from a solid, spherical cluster of cells to a hollow ball, the blastocyst, with a tiny protuberance at one spot on its inner wall. Most of this little bump, known as the inner cell mass, is destined to become the embryo proper. But the cells that make up the greater part of the blastocyst play no direct part in building the baby. They, with bits of the inner cell mass, form the embryo's contribution to the structures that will protect and nourish it for the next nine months: the chorion, the outer membrane that surrounds the embryo; the amnion, the fluid-filled sac in which it floats; and the placenta, or afterbirth, where

THE BEGINNING
The growth of every human being begins with a special cell, the ovum, shown on the opposite page magnified 2,000 times. The dark nucleus within the nutritive, yellow cytoplasm contains chromosomes from the mother. Within the protective membrane encircling the egg is a small polar body, a nonproductive sister cell which was formed as the egg matured in the ovary.

the exchange of materials takes place between mother and child.

About a week after conception, the blastocyst begins to burrow its way into the lining of the womb, attaching itself in such a fashion that the side on which the inner cell mass lies is in contact with the uterine lining. Almost immediately thereafter, its outer portion, which is known as the trophoblast, begins to grow rapidly. As it does it sends out finger-like extensions, called villi, which also work their way into the wall; simultaneously the outer portion forms the chorion. Other trophoblast cells begin to join with part of the inner cell mass to produce the amnion, the fluid content of which serves to cushion the baby against shocks or pressure from the outside world.

Protection: the first necessity for growth

During the third week, the villi proliferate enormously, and small blood vessels begin to form within them. At one end, these vessels are connected to the embryo through four larger vessels; these, with their surrounding tissues, will later become the umbilical cord. At the other end, the vessels of the villi lie within the uterine lining in close contact with the mother's bloodstream. The interlocking network of villi and uterine tissues, both profusely supplied with blood vessels, makes up the placenta. To this structure, the mother's bloodstream carries food-stuffs and oxygen, while the child's carries the waste products of its metabolism. All these substances pass through the placenta, foodstuffs and oxygen from mother to embryo, wastes from embryo to mother, who excretes them through her lungs and kidneys. In addition to serving as a distribution center, the placenta also acts as a barrier, blocking harm-ful substances that may be present in the mother's bloodstream. But the placenta does not hold back every noxious substance every time. The German-measles virus may pass it, for instance, and so may some drugs, such as thalidomide. If these agents reach the embryo at crucial periods in its development, its growth may be seriously disturbed, and the baby may be born with irreparable mental or physical defects.

Despite occasional slipups, the elaborate apparatus for protecting and nourishing the embryo works perfectly most of the time. Though no-body knows precisely how many pregnancies terminate in miscarriage, the best estimates for the United States suggest that the figure is about one in 10. This means that an embryo has about a 90 per cent chance of being born alive. Its chances of developing into a normal healthy baby are almost as good: something like 84 per cent.

Miscarriages early in pregnancy are generally the result of abnormali-ties of development, either of the embryo or of the protective and nutri-tive structures derived from the trophoblast. If the sperm or egg is de-fective, the baby is doomed from the moment of conception. Heredity

THE EMBRYO'S BRAIN rapidly evolves in complexity as it grows in size *(right)*. During the fourth week of life, the primary areas, fore-, mid-, and hindbrain, become faintly visible. Then within a period of three more weeks, the brain bulges to form its five major subdivisions *(1 through 5)*. By this time the developing brain has become sufficiently elaborate to control the embryo's first simple movements.

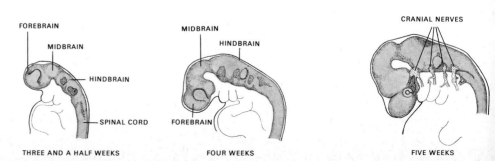

THREE AND A HALF WEEKS   FOUR WEEKS   FIVE WEEKS

may also doom the baby. Genetically speaking, nobody is perfect: the sex cells of virtually every human being contain some abnormal genes, and if those of both parents carry the same serious abnormality, the embryo may not survive. For example, the fertilized egg may develop to the blastocyst stage, but the inner cell mass may fail to emerge. Or, if it does, it may become nothing more than a disorganized bundle of tissue, whose cells have multiplied but have not differentiated properly or arranged themselves into structures. Even if the embryo develops normally, the trophoblast may not. If the villi do not form properly, the embryo will not receive adequate nourishment or oxygen, and it will die. On the other hand, if the uterine lining is imperfect, the blastocyst will be unable to implant itself firmly enough, and growth will cease.

Illness of the mother is a relatively infrequent cause of miscarriage. Only such serious disorders as severe malnutrition, chronic high blood pressure, pneumonia or typhoid fever are likely in themselves to produce an abortion. Contrary to popular belief, physical or emotional shock rarely makes a mother lose her child. The cushion of the amnion, plus the chorion and the mother's own tissues, protect the baby from all but the most extreme physical shock. In 1963 a pregnant woman in Wales was struck by lightning—and gave birth to a normal baby six months later. Emotional shock seldom upsets the mother's system sufficiently to halt the baby's development.

From the biologist's point of view, the question of why miscarriages sometimes occur is far less interesting than why they do not invariably occur. There are seemingly good biological reasons why every pregnancy should end in miscarriage. Physiologically, the embryo is a foreign substance inside its mother. Since half its genes come from the father, its genetic makeup is different from hers. And the human body does not normally tolerate the presence of any tissue that differs from it genetically in even the smallest degree. Transplants of organs such as kidneys will not "take" spontaneously unless the donor and the recipient are identical twins, who share precisely the same genes. If a piece of skin from a child is grafted onto his mother, it will degenerate in about two weeks —yet the mother tolerates the child within her for nine months.

The paradox of tolerance

Since the early 1950s, scientists have been trying to discover the nature of this paradoxical tolerance. The problem is interesting in itself, but also has eminently practical implications. If the tolerance can be reproduced artificially, organs and tissues could be transplanted from any human being to any other.

Two lines of study, each approaching the problem from a different direction, have offered important clues. One school believes that the

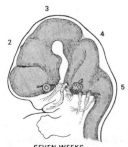

SEVEN WEEKS

trophoblast—the group of cells that is the precursor of the chorion and placenta—seems to have some special quality which permits the mother's body to accept it as a nonforeign tissue. And if the trophoblast fails to evoke a "foreign body" reaction, the chorion and placenta, which are derived from it, will presumably follow suit. These structures would thus serve to insulate the embryo against rejection by the mother. Several experiments support this theory. In one, a fertilized mouse egg was implanted on the kidney of another mouse, of a genetically different strain. Though placed in an alien environment, the embryo thrived. In a second experiment, the trophoblast of an early mouse embryo was carefully separated from the embryo proper, and each was grafted onto one of the kidneys of a second mouse, again of a different strain. The embryo quickly perished, but the trophoblast continued to grow and develop, apparently completely unaffected by its peculiar surroundings.

Blocking the mechanism of rejection

In another attack on the problem, two American physicians, James H. Nelson Jr. and J. Edward Hall of the Downstate Medical Center in New York, focused on the role of the mother rather than the trophoblast in maintaining coexistence with the embryo. In particular, they studied changes in the thymus-lymphatic system, a glandular network running throughout the body which is known to be closely involved in the rejection of foreign-tissue grafts. Earlier work had shown that in several species of small mammals the thymus-lymphatic system becomes less active during pregnancy, and does not return to normal until after the babies are born. Guided by this observation, Nelson and Hall examined lymph tissue taken from pregnant women. They found that it showed structural changes resembling those found in the animals. Lymph tissue from women who are not pregnant shows none of these characteristics, nor does tissue taken from women only a month or two after they have given birth. Apparently something happens during pregnancy that suppresses the mechanisms of rejection.

This finding raises several problems. For one thing, if the changes in the mother's lymph tissue produce tolerance for the embryo, this might presumably be matched by less resistance to other foreign bodies, such as bacteria. Yet physicians have found no evidence that pregnant women are especially prone to infections. The apparent reason is that the body has at least two sets of rejection mechanisms. Each has its own function, and suppression of one mechanism does not necessarily inactivate others. A more significant question is what suppresses a rejection mechanism, if this is what happens? To this question other studies have supplied a possible answer. Not surprisingly, it implicates the trophoblast. A hormone produced by the fetal part of the placenta—precisely that

SPECULATIVE DRAWINGS from the first midwives' guide, published in the 16th Century by the German doctor Eucharius Rosslin, shows fetuses with full heads of hair and without umbilical cords. Dissection was limited by law to only four cadavers a year, and Rosslin based most of his concepts on the theories of ancient Greek physicians.

part which the trophoblast builds—appears to play a part in damping the thymus-lymphatic system. Thus both mother and child may contribute to producing an environment that is safe for growth and development.

Given this environment, the embryo develops rapidly. By the start of the fourth week, it has already acquired a primitive nervous system with a two-lobed brain. By that time, too, a U-shaped heart has formed. The heart pumps blood through a simple system of vessels within the baby's body as well as through the blood vessels of the umbilical cord to the placenta, which is now functioning. The embryo has not yet developed any internal apparatus to manufacture its own blood. This job is performed by the yolk sac, a structure which had emerged from the embryo before the heart went into action, had developed blood vessels and begun to produce red blood cells. Until the end of the sixth week, all the baby's blood will be manufactured by the yolk sac. Then the developing liver will take over the bulk of the job, but will itself gradually be displaced by the bone marrow, which will produce red cells for the rest of the life of this human being.

With the circulatory system set up and functioning, other major structures soon emerge. In the fifth week, the arms and legs begin to develop. In another three weeks fingers and toes will be clearly visible. By the end of the seventh week, the head is recognizably human: eyes, ears, nose and mouth are present. The embryo has also become much more sensitive to stimuli, a change which reflects the phenomenal growth of its nervous system. The brain by now has developed all five of its major subdivisions, though its surface still lacks the characteristic convolutions. The stomach, which first appeared about three weeks earlier, begins to secrete gastric juices, though it contains no food. The major musculature has also formed, and the skeleton, originally made of elastic cartilage, has begun to turn to bone.

By the beginning of the ninth week, then, the baby is still incomplete but well on his way. His chances of being born alive have risen from 90 per cent to 95 per cent.

The genetic blueprints

The gross structural changes that take place during the first eight weeks of embryonic life reflect equally profound alterations in the cells that make up the embryo. The blastocyst which first implanted itself in the uterine wall has not only expanded enormously, creating millions of cells from only a few dozen, it also has given rise to cells that are entirely different in appearance and in function both from one another and from the original fertilized egg. In the eight-week embryo, liver cells are clearly distinguishable from cells of the heart; muscle cells and blood cells are not interchangeable; bone cells cannot do the work of brain

THE SNUG FIT of a baby about to be born feet first—the "breech" position—is accurately indicated in this picture from a 1751 treatise on midwifery. One of England's great animal painters, George Stubbs, did the engraving. A thorough man, Stubbs "snatched" the corpse of a pregnant woman and made drawings from a clandestine dissection.

cells, or brain cells act as bone.

Yet all these cells contain exactly the same genes. Except for the sperm and the egg, every cell in the body has a full complement of hereditary material and thus is potentially capable of performing the functions of any kind of cell. As the embryo develops, however, the cells begin to specialize, "learning" to act on only one of these many possible sets of instructions. This process takes place gradually; little by little the possibilities are narrowed down until at last the cell achieves its permanent and, for the most part, irreversible character.

The embryonic sandwich

Cellular specialization progresses with a speed paralleling that of the structural changes. A mere two weeks after conception, the inner cell mass has already developed three distinct groups of cells, neatly arranged in a three-layered sandwich, which have, so to speak, divided up the body's structures among them. The top layer (the ectoderm) will give rise to the nervous system and all the outer coatings of the body: the epidermis, the hair, the fingernails. The middle layer (the mesoderm) will form the musculature, the bones and the cartilage, as well as the heart, veins and arteries. The bottom layer (the endoderm) will produce glands and the linings of such internal organs as the stomach and lungs.

Along with differentiation come two other equally basic cellular processes which shape the body's structures. Cells may change their position or migrate from one embryonic site to another; they may also multiply at different rates, producing a bulge at one place, a hollow at another. Like differentiation, these processes take place gradually. The shifting and multiplying of cells first block out rough shapes, then refine and elaborate them into finished organs.

The first step in this sculpturing process is the formation of the notochord. This structure, a rodlike primitive spine, develops from a group of mesodermal cells. Above the notochord, ectodermal cells multiply furiously to create a thickened strip, which then curls up into a tube that is the precursor of the spinal cord and brain. Meanwhile, cells from the mesoderm arrange themselves on either side of the notochord in paired blocks called somites, which will eventually develop into the vertebrae and muscles of the back. Together, these changes supply the embryo with a back and a front, as well as a fore-and-aft axis along which organ systems can arrange themselves. These, in turn, are formed by the same interweaving of processes of differentiation, movement and growth (described in more detail in the picture essay following this chapter). The digestive system, for example, begins as a tube of mesodermal cells lined with cells from the endoderm. As the tube is forming, groups of cells along its length begin to specialize, giving rise to the esophagus, the

"PREFORMED" EMBRYOS, published in 1671 by the Dutch physician Theodore Kerckring, were supposed to represent, from left to right, an opened egg at two weeks, and the skeletons of three- and six-week-old embryos. Kerckring subscribed to the theory of preformation, prevalent in the 17th and 18th Centuries, which held that the human embryo was completely formed at the moment of conception.

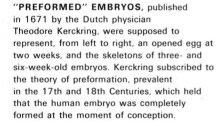

stomach, the liver, the pancreas and the intestines. A pocket branching off from the same tube develops into the lungs and trachea.

The whole process of development seems so extraordinary that early investigators in embryology, studying it under the microscope, refused to credit the evidence of their own eyes. It seemed more reasonable to suppose that the parts of the embryo did not develop but rather were present at the moment of conception, and simply unfolded, like a Japanese paper flower in water. Charles Bonnet, an 18th Century Swiss scientist, put it this way: "All the constituent parts of the body are so directly, so variously, so manifoldly intertwined as regards their functions . . . their relationship is so tight and so indivisible, that they must have originated all together at one and the same time. The artery implies the veins, their operation implies the nerves, which in their turn imply the brain and that by consequence the heart, and every single condition a whole row of other conditions."

This point of view, known as preformationism, dominated scientific thought throughout the 18th Century, even though the evidence to refute it was already on hand at the time Bonnet was writing his statement. In 1759 a young German zoologist, Kaspar Friedrich Wolff, had published a report on the development of chick embryos, which he had observed under the microscope. His work made it eminently clear that the fertilized egg does not contain a minuscule chicken, and that the embryo changes radically in form as it grows. But Wolff's findings were attacked by the preformationists, and the point of view he espoused—that the structures of the embryo develop in succession—did not achieve general acceptance until early in the 19th Century. And even when Wolff's concept, which came to be called epigenesis, was accepted, the mechanisms through which epigenesis comes about were a long way from being understood. First, embryology had to be transformed from a largely descriptive to a truly experimental science.

The birth of experimental embryology

The transformation was not easy. Living organisms of any kind are difficult to work with: they change constantly, literally under the experimenter's hands. And the living organisms with which embryology deals are the most difficult of all to manipulate. They are so vulnerable that even the slightest damage can completely upset the course of their development. Mammalian embryos, moreover, can never be examined in anything approaching their normal uterine environment, and abnormal surroundings in themselves can distort the pattern of growth. Not until the 1920s did refinements of technique make it possible to keep monkey and rabbit embryos alive briefly outside the mother's body, and thus to watch the early stages of their development in the laboratory. Even

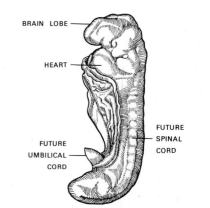

BRAIN LOBE

HEART

FUTURE
UMBILICAL
CORD

FUTURE
SPINAL
CORD

AN ACTUAL EMBRYO, three weeks old, disproves the preformationists' notion that it contains all the body's parts fully developed in miniature. Actually, it is a soft, bulging lump of tissue without any kind of skeleton and composed of only rudimentary parts *(above)*. A mere tenth of an inch long, the budding embryo nonetheless has a pulsating heart and two-lobed brain. Other portions will later form the spinal and umbilical cords.

today no methods have yet been devised to raise full-grown test-tube babies of any species, let alone keep them alive after "birth."

In 1887, when the first systematic experiments in embryology were begun, the techniques available were still extremely crude, and the only embryos that could be worked with were those of creatures such as sea urchins or frogs, which normally develop outside the mother's body in a watery environment that could be duplicated in the laboratory. Frogs' eggs were used by the pioneer experimental embryologist, a German named Wilhelm Roux. One of Roux's initial aims was to find experimental support for one of the then-current theories of how heredity shapes embryological development. According to this theory, advanced by another German, the biologist August Weismann, the hereditary material in the fertilized egg is progressively divided up in the process of cell division, so that by the time the organism is born, each cell carries only one piece of hereditary information. This information consists of the instructions required to produce one particular type of cell. A heart cell would thus carry only heart-cell information, a brain cell only instructions to build a brain cell. Only the sex cells would retain a complete set of instructions.

Carrying Weismann's hypothesis further, Roux theorized that of the two cells produced by the first cleavage of the fertilized egg, one should contain determinants for all the structures on the right side of the body, while the other should contain determinants for structures on the left side. The second cleavage, occurring at right angles to the first, would then segregate the determinants for the upper half of the body from those of the lower half. Each successive division would reduce the number of determinants per cell and, at the same time, segregate them one from another. Roux also believed that the developments in each cell took place independently of what was happening in every other cell; that is, no part of the developing embryo was in any way influenced by events occurring in any other part.

Wilhelm Roux's tadpoles

To put this theory to the test, Roux took fertilized frogs' eggs immediately after their first cleavage and pierced one of the two cells in each with a red-hot needle. Though only 20 per cent of the eggs survived this drastic treatment, all of the survivors appeared to confirm his point of view. For the brief period that they continued to develop they resembled nothing so much as half-embryos—developing tadpoles split down the middle.

Roux's experiments fascinated the scientific world, and other investigators hastened to try to duplicate them. One of them, Hans Driesch, a German working in a Naples laboratory, undertook a somewhat dif-

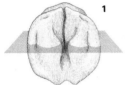

FOREBRAIN AT 24 DAYS

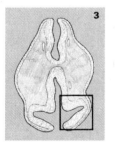

CROSS SECTION

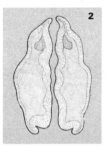

BRAIN AT 25 DAYS

FORMATION OF THE EYE is shown here, beginning with the swelling that appears on the embryo's forebrain (1—front view) around the 24th day. In cross section (2) the swelling is seen as a slight projection on the surface. It enlarges to form a bulge called the optical vesicle (3), which eventually will form the optic nerve, retina, iris and coatings of the eyeball. The vesicle continues to bulge outward from the brain (4), then folds in upon itself (5) to make a cradle for the future lens, now forming on the surface of the head. The cradle deepens to surround the lens (6). By the end of the sixth week, the lens has separated from the surface (7). A week later (8), eyelids have started to form and the main elements of the eye have been established.

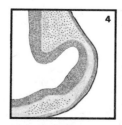

30 DAYS

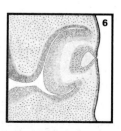

34 DAYS

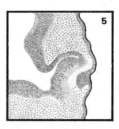

38 DAYS

ferent version of the same work. Driesch experimented on sea-urchin eggs, using a technique for separating them that was somewhat less drastic than Roux's. Instead of piercing the cells with a hot needle, Driesch put a group of eggs that had reached the two-cell stage into a bottle and shook them until the clusters separated into individual cells. "In order to obtain results," he noted, "one must shake as vigorously as possible for five minutes or more." He then placed the cells in small dishes filled with seawater and left them overnight.

Hans Driesch's sea urchins

"I awaited in excitement the picture which was to present itself in my dishes the next day," he later wrote. "I must confess that the idea of a freeswimming hemisphere or even a half [embryo] with its [gut] opened lengthwise seemed rather extraordinary. I thought the formations would probably die. Instead, however, the following morning I found typical, actively swimming [embryos] of half size."

Driesch repeated his experiment, using embryos that had reached the four-, the eight- or even the 16-cell stage. Shaken free, the individual cells still developed into complete embryos. Clearly, even after the fertilized egg had split several times, every cell still contained all the necessary information for the production of a complete organism. The results, of course, flatly contradicted Roux's findings, which Driesch believed to have been caused by primitive technique: the pierced cell, still hanging on to the live one, had somehow impeded its development.

Driesch's experiments not only cast doubt on the validity of Roux's theory, but also raised some new and fundamental questions. How could half of an embryo, or three quarters or even 15/16, proceed to a normal development? If the hereditary material was not parceled out to the different cells, how did they "learn" to differentiate and form themselves into structures?

It was still another German, Hans Spemann, who provided the first answers to these questions. Spemann proved conclusively that the development of the fertilized egg is determined not merely by the genetic material in its nucleus, but also by an interplay between this material and the rest of the cell. Moreover, he discovered, the principle of interplay operates throughout the development of the embryo. Each successive step in cell differentiation and the development of structure is influenced by surrounding cells and is the result of steps taken before.

Spemann died in 1941, only six years after he received the Nobel Prize for Medicine for his "discovery of the organizer effect in embryonic development." To the study of this principle he devoted more than 30 years of his professional career. Viewed superficially, his experiments seem very narrow in scope. Most of them concerned the development of

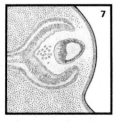

40 DAYS

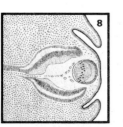

49 DAYS

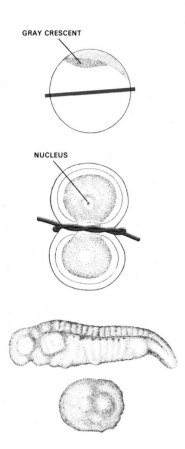

GRAY CRESCENT

NUCLEUS

A SPEMANN EXPERIMENT early in the 20th Century revealed the cellular elements that determine whether or not an egg becomes an embryo. The German zoologist divided a newt's egg in two by tying a strand of baby's hair around it, leaving a protoplasmic bridge between the halves. Nuclear material passed over the bridge, starting cell division in both halves, but only one half developed into a normal newt: the half containing an area called the gray crescent. The other half, lacking a gray crescent, became a disorganized mass of cells.

certain organs, such as the eye in the newt embryo, but their theoretical implications were far wider.

When Spemann began his experiments on the newt eye, he already knew its developmental timetable. The eyes begin as two small swellings on the embryonic newt's brain. These push through the surrounding tissue and press outward against the coat of ectoderm that encases the embryo. Soon the swellings change form, turning into mushroom-shaped structures with stalks running to the brain and caps close to the embryo's outer skin. The caps begin to dent inward at the center, to produce a double-walled cup. The inner wall of this optic cup eventually forms the light-sensitive cells of the retina, while the outer wall forms the protective layers of tissue that cover most of the eyeball. While the retina is being formed, the outer coat of ectoderm is also changing. Moving inward to follow the shape of the eye cup, it gradually becomes transformed into the lens, which will focus light rays entering the eye. After the optic cup and lens have emerged, the protective window, the cornea, develops. This is the step-by-step process by which the eye is formed.

Development through induction

Spemann discovered that an eye can be grown in this manner virtually anywhere on the surface of the developing embryo, not just in the head. For example, when Spemann placed the eye cup from the head of a newt embryo just under the ectoderm of the animal's belly, the ectoderm cells of the belly promptly formed themselves into a lens. The embryo soon had an eye growing in its belly. Clearly, ectodermal cells far from the head region could be made to form a lens.

Further experiments showed that similar processes, which Spemann called "induction," operated at the very earliest stages of development. Making use of a technique developed by a colleague, Oscar Hertwig, Spemann looped a strand of baby's hair around a fertilized newt egg before its first cleavage and tightened the loop so that the egg was forced into the shape of an hourglass. Soon the egg cleaved and the two halves separated—but the fate of the two halves seemed unpredictable. Sometimes both developed into normal embryos. At other times one developed normally while the other produced only a disorganized blob of tissue which died. This unpredictability was not caused by Spemann's technique. The critical factor was the composition of the separated cells. When both contained a nucleus and a section of the surrounding cytoplasm called the gray crescent, both developed normally. If only one of these elements was present, development was invariably abnormal. Both were necessary if the egg was to become an embryo.

This was Spemann's major discovery: that at every stage of embryonic development, structures already present act as organizers, inducing the emergence of whatever structures are next on the timetable. In the fertilized newt egg, the gray crescent is the forerunner. As the egg divides, the group of cells derived from this area of the egg becomes the "primary organizer," galvanizing other cells to shape themselves into specific forms. The organizer cells themselves become the notochord and the somites. The notochord and the somites induce the ectoderm to form the neural tube, from which in turn the brain and spinal cord develop.

Spemann became certain that he was right when he found that the primary organizer will induce the formation of later structures even after the process of development is fairly well under way. In one experiment, he transplanted the organizer cells from one young newt embryo to a second. The result was a set of embryonic Siamese twins. The graft induced formation of a secondary embryo upon the first, an embryo complete with spinal column, head, trunk, legs and tail. Some of its tissues came from the graft cells, but others came from the host cells. This happened even when the graft and the host were of different species.

Human development is shaped by essentially the same forces that Spemann discovered in newts. Science does not yet know what part of the human egg corresponds to the gray crescent in the newt, but it has tentatively identified the structure in the embryo that acts as the primary organizer. The structure, called the "primitive streak," is a group of ectodermal cells that emerges at one end of the embryo about the 12th day after conception. It is from the primitive streak that the mesoderm develops, and it is from the mesoderm that the first embryonic structures—the notochord and somites—are built. And as in newts, so in humans, it is the notochord and its associated structures that organize the rest of the embryo.

Obviously, then, an embryonic cell is influenced by the other cells in its environment, which gradually lead it to act on only one of the many possible sets of instructions that it contains. Once these instructions have been issued, however, and the cell has assumed a specific character, it cannot "change its mind." When a gray crescent is transplanted to an embryo that is well along in its development, nothing happens. The developmental process has gone too far to be changed.

The end of an eight-week journey

The interplay between the genes and their environment was demonstrated even more dramatically by a pupil of Spemann's, Otto Mangold. Mangold worked with two kinds of salamanders, the axolotl and the newt. These two creatures are somewhat different from each other even in the embryonic stage. The newt embryo has antennalike structures, called balancers, near its mouth. The axolotl does not. When Mangold transplanted belly skin from an axolotl embryo to the face of a newt

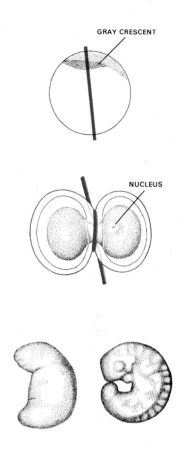

GRAY CRESCENT

NUCLEUS

IN ANOTHER EXPERIMENT Spemann developed two perfect embryos when he tied a strand of baby's hair around a newt's egg so that part of the gray crescent fell in each half. The half containing the nucleus of the egg developed on schedule, but the other half lagged slightly behind because, at the outset, it had no nucleus. Eventually nuclear material from cell division which had occurred in the first half of the newt's egg migrated across the protoplasmic bridge to start cell division in the second half. After that, it too formed a newt.

embryo, it developed into head tissue, but without balancers. On the other hand, when he reversed the process and transplanted newt belly skin onto the face of an axolotl, balancers developed. Evidently the newt embryo could make head tissue out of tissue that would normally have become belly skin, but could not force it to form balancers, because the axolotl cells did not contain instructions for doing so. But when an axolotl embryo induced newt skin to form head tissue, the balancers appeared, since instructions for them were built into the newt cells. Though inducting substances can galvanize development even outside their own species, the only kind of development they can trigger is that for which the receiving organism already has genetic blueprints.

All these experiments have shed new light on the embryo's eight-week journey from egg to miniature baby. In a sense, both the epigenetic and the preformationist points of view are true. Many characteristics of each human being are determined, at the very moment of conception, by the united genetic material of an egg and a sperm. This material will in large measure establish the way the individual develops, not merely during his first eight weeks but long afterward. But the order and timing of development are set by the interaction of this genetic material with its environment. Cells are shaped by the cells around them, and their collective, interacting development shapes the growing baby.

Creating an Organism with Cells

The study of growth between conception and birth is remarkably well documented. Scientists know that the multiplication of cells enlarges the organism, that the movement of groups of cells helps shape the organism, and that differentiation alters the form and function of cells to prepare them for different duties. They know that some cells must die to help shape the living organism. The chromosomes, and specifically their elusive components, the genes, are known to play the role of planners and supervisors. To gather this information, scientists have observed the growth of human fetuses where possible, and supplemented their study with experiments on animals. To illustrate their findings, they have resorted to a variety of techniques, such as the diagrams, drawings and photomicrographs shown on the following pages. Still remaining at the bottom of the ever-increasing body of knowledge is the persistent question: "How?"

A TRIUMVIRATE OF BODY BUILDERS
The three processes through which the body develops and grows—the multiplication, movement and differentiation of cells—may be thought of as lying at the points of a triangle (opposite). Guided by the genes, each of the processes exerts the necessary influence at exactly the right moments of development, working, separately or in concert, steadily to complete the product, a human being.

MULTIPLICATION

MOVEMENT

DIFFERENTIATION

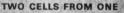

ZONA PELLUCIDA

FERTILIZED EGG

NUCLEUS

IN THE BEGINNING
A fertilized egg, called a zygote *(shown in cross section at left)*, begins the business of multiplication soon after fertilization. Surrounding the zygote is the *zona pellucida*, a thin, temporary membrane which holds together the mass of cells produced by the multiplication process.

TWO CELLS FROM ONE
The first multiplication, in which the zygote splits in two, is completed within 36 hours. The daughter cells are identical to the zygote in every respect, but are only half its size.

MORE BUT SMALLER
By the fourth day, the *zona pellucida* is packed with several dozen cells. All are substantially smaller than the zygote from which they are descended, but remain otherwise identical.

THE START OF MOVEMENT
On the fifth day, cell movement begins. The cells in the outer ring will form the placenta. Those clumped at the right, called the inner cell mass, are the beginnings of the embryo itself.

The Simple Beginnings

During the first two weeks of human development the cellular processes of growth—multiplication, movement and differentiation—are at their simplest and most comprehensible. The multiplication begins almost at the moment of conception, and for the first few days is the only process in operation. Cells are reproduced in a geometric progression, one cell dividing into two, then two into four and so on. As the embryo grows, cell movement begins to organize the mass of cells, first into an irregular hollow ball, then into more elaborate shapes such as the embryonic disc, which sets the stage for the third process, differentiation. It is uncer-

THE EMBRYONIC DISC

By the 12th day the inner cell mass has rearranged itself to form a two-layered disc. Of the two cavities, one will soon shrink, while the other will act as a fluid-filled protective cushion.

READY FOR DIFFERENTIATION

By the beginning of the third week, the embryonic disc has grown from two layers to three *(below)*. Each layer will develop into a different set of organs and tissues *(right)*, though there are still no detectable differences among the cells.

ECTODERM

MESODERM

ENDODERM

THE THREE-LAYERED DISC: FOUNDATION OF THE MAN

ECTODERM, THE OUTER LAYER

Not surprisingly, cells from this section of the disc form the body's outermost tissues, the skin, hair and nails. But some will develop into the brain and the rest of the nervous system.

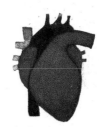

MESODERM, THE MIDDLE LAYER

This group of cells will develop into the skeleton and bone marrow, the muscles, heart and blood corpuscles, and also form the inner skin layer, the blood vessels, kidneys and gonads.

ENDODERM, THE INNER LAYER

From these cells will spring the linings of nearly all of the internal organs, including those of the lungs, trachea and pharynx, and digestive tract including the pancreas and the liver.

tain at just what point differentiation begins its irrevocable changes by which the cells are gradually modified for specific functions. But by the end of the second week, groups of cells have embarked on the different paths which will eventually result in the specializations necessary for the formation of the mature organism.

43

Embryonic Disc to Working Tissue

Perhaps the least understood of the various processes of development is differentiation. In searching for an analogy to the mechanisms of development, biologist John Tyler Bonner of Princeton University has compared multiplication to the work of a sculptor "who continually adds clay to make a shape," and cell movement to the "pushing and the modeling of the clay." But there the analogy ends, for there is no process, either natural or man-made, that parallels the invisible chemical changes within developing cells that bring about vastly differing forms and functions.

Without differentiation a complex organism such as man could not exist. By producing cells with specific abilities to perform specific jobs, differentiation makes possible a division of labor within the body. The cells that form heart muscle, for example, would be ill adapted to do the work of the lungs or nervous system.

About all that can be said with certainty about differentiation is that it is gradual. But although the mechanisms of differentiation remain largely mysterious, its manifestations are omnipresent. They are readily observable in the generation of the great variety of organs and structures, such as the heart and lungs (right), from different layers of the embryonic disc.

THE ENDODERM

THE LUNGS
The lungs, like many internal organs, are composed of cells that spring from more than one layer of the embryonic disc. They begin their development with a thick lining of endoderm cells (opposite, left), which becomes steadily thinner as the lungs grow. After birth, the air tubes are expanded (far right), and the lining of the tiny air sacs has become thin enough to permit inhaled oxygen to be transferred to the blood in exchange for carbon dioxide.

THE MESODERM

THE HEART
Since the fetus must draw sustenance from the mother's bloodstream early in development, the heart and circulatory system becomes the first functioning system in the body. By the fourth week the system is operational, though rudimentary. Like almost every other muscle, the heart is formed from mesodermal cells. Its mature form is achieved by the eighth week, although the development of individual cells (opposite, left) is not nearly complete (far right).

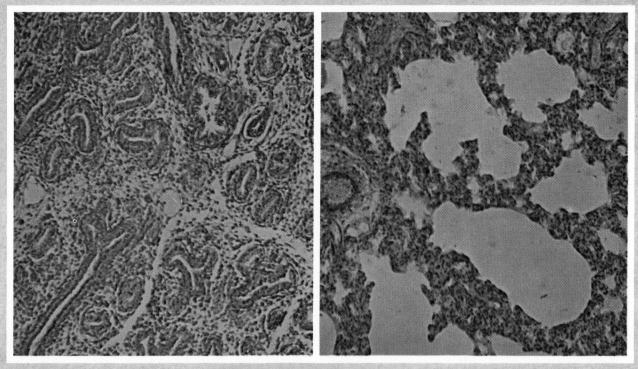

The lighter areas of lung tissue in a 12-week embryo *(left)* become enlarged after birth *(right)*, when respiration fills the lungs with air.

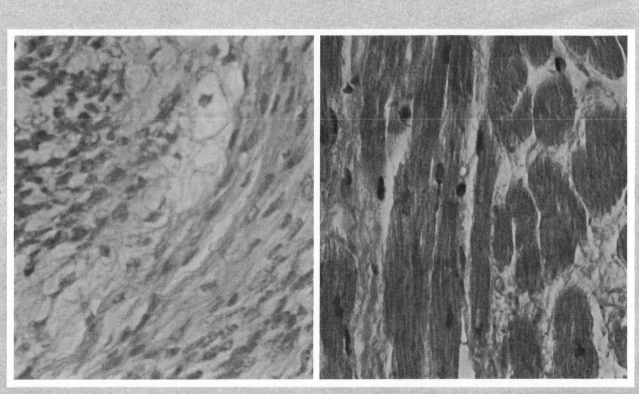

In the third month *(left)*, heart cells are poorly defined, and are noticeably narrower than those of a mature heart muscle *(right)*.

Forming the Network of Nerves

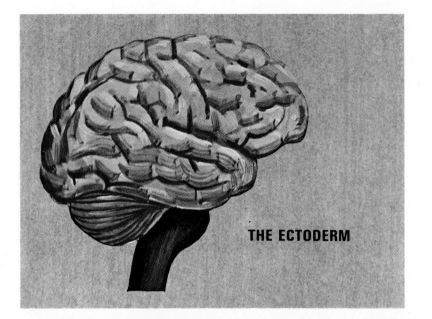

THE ECTODERM

The nervous system, the body's complex communications network, starts to develop during the third week. Its progenitor is a section of ectoderm called the neural plate *(bottom left)*. The entire system evolves from this plate: massive structures like the brain *(left)* as well as the delicate fibers of motor neurons *(right)*. The full complement of nerve cells—at least 10 billion in humans—is present by the time of birth. From that time on, no new nerve cells will be added—existing cells will enlarge to keep pace with the normal growth of the body.

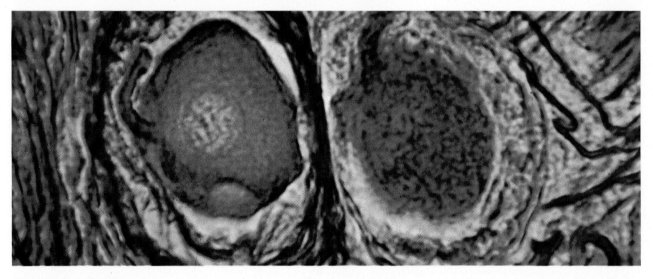

CELLS OF THE SENSES

Two sensory neurons, which were formed in the neural crest *(3, below)*, appear above in their mature state. The cells are unipolar: they have only one fiber attached to the cell body. In the photomicrograph above, the fibers extend to the left of each cell. Outside the cell body the fiber divides. One extension goes to the skin or other sensory area to pick up stimuli, the other transmits the stimuli to the spinal cord.

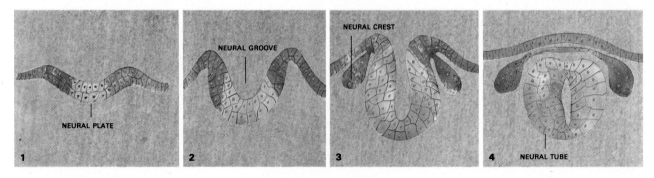

BIRTH OF THE NERVOUS SYSTEM

The development of the neural plate, illustrated in cross section about 150 times actual size, shows how cell movement molds a complex structure from a single layer of cells. First the plate thickens and bulges downward (1). The bulge enlarges (2 and 3) until the edges of the plate, along with the cells at the tips of the folds, fuse (4), forming the neural tube and two rows of cells. The tube *(yellow)* forms the brain and spinal cord, including motor neurons *(opposite)*. The rust-colored layer gives rise to sensory cells *(above)*, and the top layer *(pink)* will become skin.

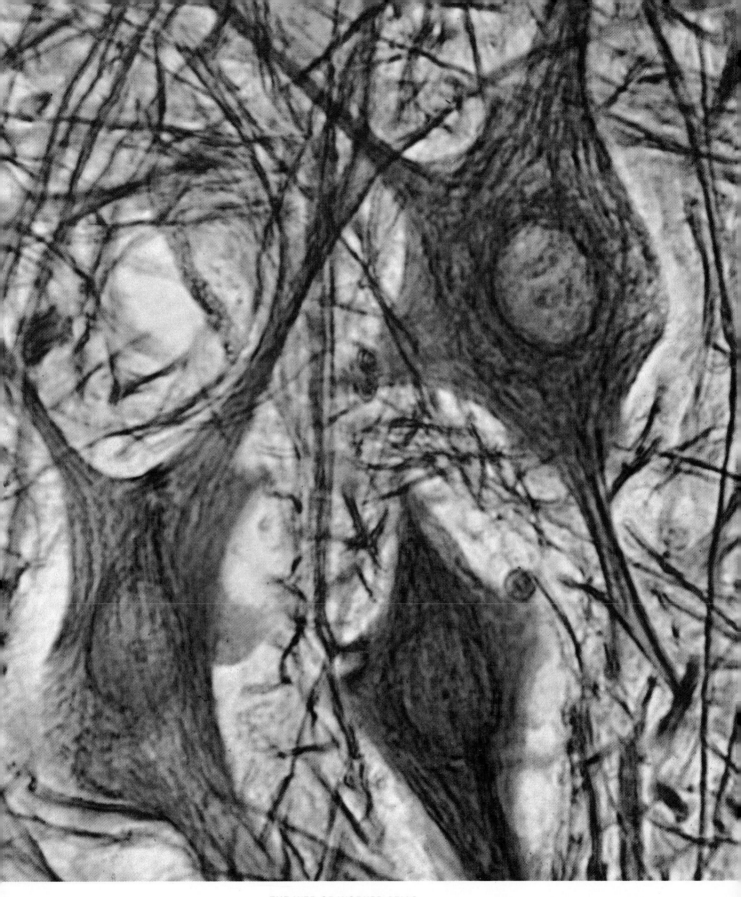

THE WEB OF WORKER CELLS

Three motor neurons, products of the neural tube, stand out against their conducting fibers in the spinal cord. Unlike the sensory neurons opposite, which receive impulses from only one site, the motor neuron's many fibers pick up instructions from thousands of sources in the brain and spinal cord. A single output fiber carries the message to activate the muscles.

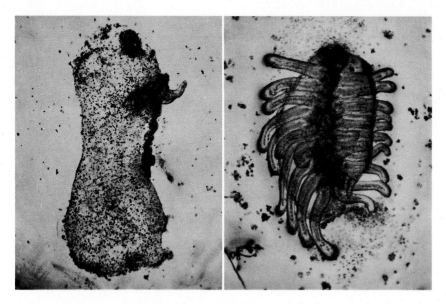

CELLS THAT HELP OTHER CELLS
Clear evidence of induction is provided in these photographs of skin taken from a chicken embryo. When French biologists Etienne Wolff and Philippe Sengel grew skin tissue in a culture without nerve cells, the resulting skin was bald *(far left)*. Another fragment of skin from the same embryo, kept alive in a culture of brain extract, sprouted feathers on schedule *(left)*.

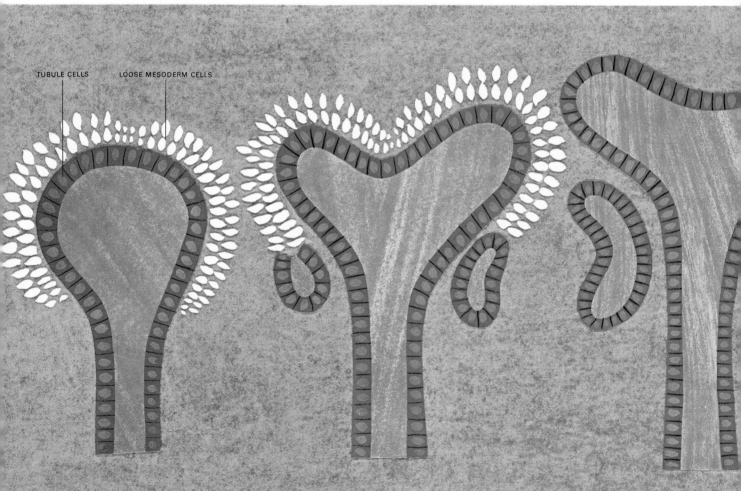

TUBULE CELLS   LOOSE MESODERM CELLS

INTERACTION BUILDS A KIDNEY
Kidney tubules, tiny tubes which extract wastes from the bloodstream and pass them to the bladder, begin to form in the sixth week as two types of mesodermal cell begin to interact.

BRANCHING BEGINS
By the seventh week the loose mesoderm cells around the immature tubule cause it to branch out. Simultaneously the tubule cells influence the loose cells to form two spherical masses.

REACHING FOR UNITY
During differentiation both the tubule and its two associated groups of cells have enlarged. Interaction continues to operate, stimulating the three bodies to grow toward one another.

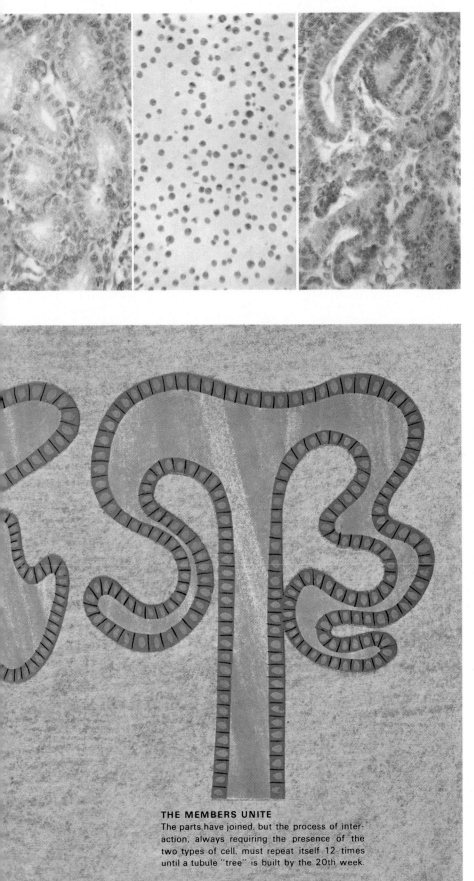

To demonstrate that certain cells retain the ability to interact even when the structure they have formed is destroyed, biologist Aron A. Moscona experimented with nearly mature kidney tissue from a chick embryo. The tissue *(left)* was broken into a disorganized group of cells *(center)*, which soon regrouped, forming a new tissue remarkably like the original *(right)*.

THE MEMBERS UNITE
The parts have joined, but the process of interaction, always requiring the presence of the two types of cell, must repeat itself 12 times until a tubule "tree" is built by the 20th week.

The Importance of Control

Development, which is initiated by changes in the structure or location of individual cells or cell groups, soon comes under the control of more sophisticated processes in which cells must interact with one another. Following a genetically preset schedule, a cell or group of cells releases substances that cause neighboring cells to embark on a new course of development, a process called induction. In the embryonic chick, for example, skin cells will not differentiate into feather cells until nerve cells are also present *(opposite, above)*. In human beings, two relatively unspecialized types of cell unite to form kidney tubules—but only in the presence of each other *(left)*.

Cellular interaction not only induces individual cells to differentiate, but also prompts groups of cells to arrange themselves into functioning organs *(above)*. These interactions are a fundamental part of orderly development, for nerves, muscles, bones and blood do not function in isolation. Each must be ready at the right time and in the right place for the growing organism to survive.

A CHANGE IN SHAPE

The metamorphosis of the Southern bullfrog provides a spectacular example of the role of cell death. For three to six months after hatching, the tadpole grows but retains its fishlike shape. After attaining full growth its tail cells begin to die off. The tail shrinks steadily until, 15 months after hatching, the tadpole has become a frog. For the remainder of its life, the frog continues to grow but its shape does not alter.

Death to Form the Living

The mass production of new cells is so obviously important to growth that it tends to obscure an equally significant process. Surprisingly, destruction rather than production of cells is the determining factor in shaping some parts of the embryo.

Cell death is most crucial, and is most dramatically demonstrated, in major reorganizations of form such as the metamorphosis of a tadpole into a frog *(opposite)*, or the transformation of a stubby chunk of tissue into a highly organized limb *(right)*. But it is as important in human embryos, whose hands and feet first appear as solid lumps; the sculpting of the fingers and toes requires the death of many thousands of cells.

These "sacrifices" seem to be accomplished in several ways. In the metamorphosis of the frog, each tail cell is believed to contain a sort of "suicide capsule," a sac of enzymes which, when released, destroy the cell. The causes of cell death in the human embryo have not yet been determined. Another unanswered question is what happens to dead cells, although there is some evidence that their chemicals are reprocessed to speed the development of new cells.

SCULPTING WINGS AND FEET

Using a dye that stains only dead cells, scientists can easily spot areas of degeneration in the wing and foot buds of a four-day-old chick embryo *(above)*. The degeneration aids in shaping the wings and feet of the newborn chick *(top)*. Even when particular cells scheduled for destruction are transplanted to another part of the embryo, they die at their appointed time.

Chromosomes: The Ultimate Secret

Every process of growth, from multiplication to cell death, is ultimately controlled by the genes, which lie in stringlike chromosomes and "instruct" the cell in its duties. But what controls the genes? Cells that assume different forms and functions must be receiving different instructions. The processes that activate one gene while inhibiting others are still unexplained, but biologists are turning up clues.

The first clue came from researchers studying the midge *Chironomus tentans*. They found that the chromosomes taken from a particular organ were puffed out at one point *(opposite and below)*. They concluded that the puffs must consist of activated genes. Molecules of deoxyribonucleic acid (DNA), which constitute the genes'

coded instructions, were at that moment supervising the manufacture of ribonucleic acid (RNA), the messenger which conveys the instructions to the body of the cell. Later experiments have shown that in some cases a particular hormone quickens specific genes into activity. For example, when a *Chironomus* is injected with a hormone that induces molting, chromosome puffs form within 30 minutes, incidentally pinpointing the location of the genes that control the molting process. More experiments will be needed before man achieves a complete understanding of these secrets of development. When that happens, however, he may be able to exercise far more precise control over the growth of domesticated plants and animals—and even over himself.

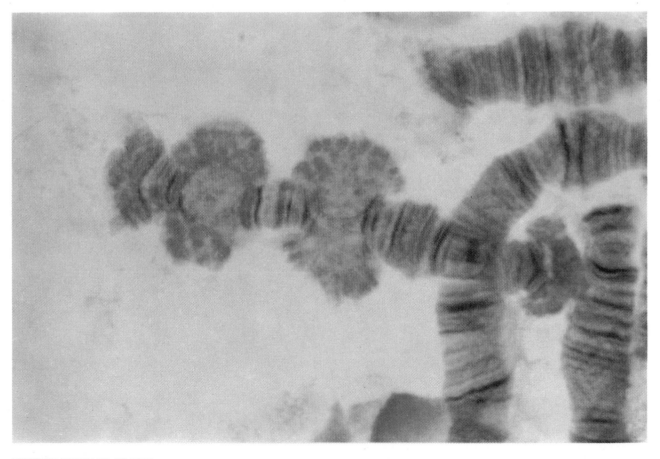

TWISTED THREADS OF LIFE
Giant chromosomes from a salivary-gland cell of a *Chironomus tentans* show concentrations of DNA stained brown, and puffed-up areas where certain genes of this particular chromosome have been "activated" to direct some specific function of the cell. The green areas indicate the presence of a protein, whose function, though believed to be important, is not known.

A PUFF OF A DIFFERENT COLOR
In another *Chironomus* chromosome, a stain colors DNA blue *(opposite)*, and reveals the presence of RNA *(purple)* in the puff. Presumably this RNA, duplicating the DNA's code, will carry instructions to the outer portion of the cell to direct the cell's various chemical activities.

3
The Next
Seven Months

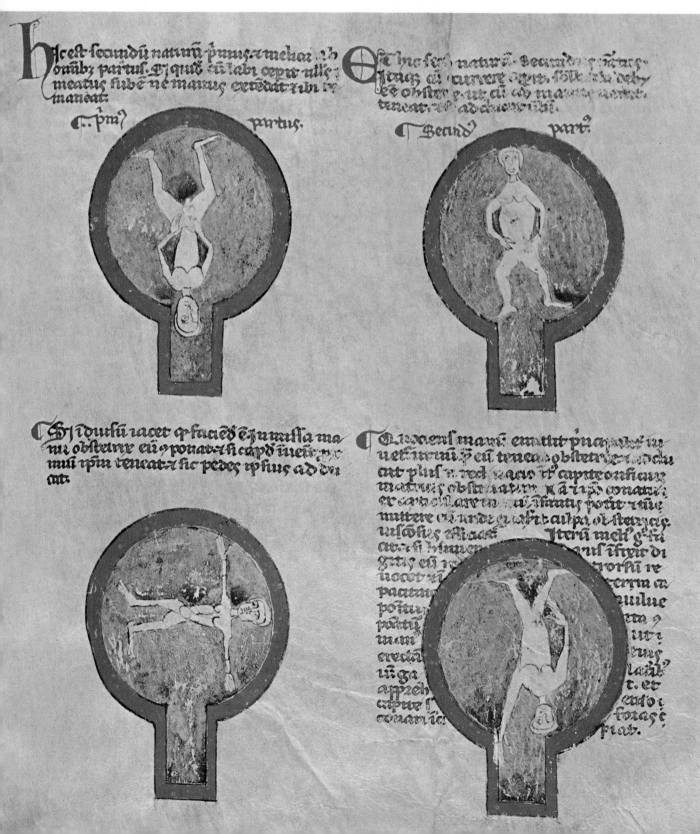

BY THE NINTH WEEK of uterine life, the growing baby has moved so far along the road to birth that it can no longer be called by its original name. During its first two months in the womb, it was an embryo—a swelling within its mother. Now it has become a fetus—an offspring. The cartilage has begun to turn to bone, the skeleton is emerging, and all the vital organs have been outlined and formed. Much more growing remains to be done, and much refinement of structure is yet to be accomplished. But the emphasis has shifted radically. From here on, the development of function becomes the most important part of the process of growth. The seven months still separating the fetus from birth are primarily months of practice, months in which the baby's body learns to use all the intricate and delicate equipment it has been building as it grows.

The answer to the question, "Will the baby be a boy or a girl?" will probably remain concealed until the moment of birth. If for some reason the physician suspects a congenital malformation in the baby, he may test his suspicion by taking a sample of the amniotic fluid. Because this fluid contains a few of the baby's cells, he may then be able to determine the infant's sex. From the very beginning, distinct differences exist between the cells of males and females. But the amniotic fluid is rarely sampled and so conjecture is all that is left. A contemporary superstition has it that the arrival of a boy is heralded by good disposition on the part of the mother during pregnancy, a girl's presence by a moody and moping mother. But this is no more valid than the ancient Hindu theory that the mother's right breast and eye enlarged if she was carrying a boy.

Although the infant's sex is determined at the moment of conception, the reproductive system does not begin to develop until the second month. Once it does, however, progress is so rapid that the differences between the sexes are unmistakable by the time the embryo has become a fetus.

The gonads, or sex glands, develop in the sixth or seventh week, appearing on either side of the abdominal cavity as paired blocks of tissue, with the same structure in both sexes. By the ninth week they have differentiated into testes and ovaries. The formation of these primary sex organs sets the stage for the development of the rest of the structures that make up the reproductive system.

By the end of the second month, the embryo has manufactured two pairs of tubes, all four roughly parallel with one another. One set is known as the Wolffian ducts, after Kaspar Friedrich Wolff, and the other as the Müllerian ducts, after Johannes Müller, a German biologist. If the baby is a boy, the newly formed testes stimulate the Wolffian ducts to develop further into several structures which include the *vas deferens,*

A PIONEER WORK IN OBSTETRICS
This page from a medieval Latin manuscript is based on the work of Soranos, the eminent Second Century Greek gynecologist who promoted the idea that it was safe for babies to be delivered feet first. He also taught midwives how to handle babies who were in unusual positions in the womb, thus saving countless mothers and children from injury and death.

the route along which the sperm will be carried. As these ducts develop, the Müllerian ducts fade away to stubs. On the other hand, if the baby is a girl, the Müllerian ducts grow into the Fallopian tubes, the uterus and the upper part of the vagina. At the same time, the Wolffian ducts fade away. These internal structures, once formed, lead to the development of the external sex organs.

Virtually weightless, still tiny

The most powerful influence on the formation of the reproductive system seems to be the hormones manufactured by the testes. This conclusion is suggested by examination of defective human fetuses: when the testes fail to form properly, the rest of the reproductive system develops along female lines. And it has been confirmed by several ingenious experiments. In one extraordinarily delicate operation, A. Jost of the Collège de France in Paris managed to remove the testes from the fetuses of male rabbits immediately after their formation, and at the same time to keep the tiny creatures alive. Thereafter, the fetuses followed a completely feminine course of development. On the other hand, when Jost removed the ovaries from the fetuses of female rabbits, their development continued unaltered.

By the fourth month, the entire reproductive system has been formed, and the fetus has begun to show that it is active and alive. The salivary glands have started working; peristalsis, the wavelike contractions that will in the future move food through the intestine, has begun; the kidneys have begun to function, discharging waste into the amniotic fluid. The four-month fetus will curl its fingers when its palm is tickled, curl its toes when it is tickled on the soles of its feet, and can even grip things with fingers and thumb. But it still could not survive outside of the womb.

Within its warm and protected world, however, it has a marvelous ease of movement. Suspended in the fluid that fills the amniotic sac, the fetus is virtually weightless. Still tiny—no more than eight to 10 inches long—and weak, it can nevertheless perform many feats that will be far beyond its capacity for months after it is born. Unlike the four-month baby, the four-month fetus can bend sharply from the hips and from the waist; it can twist its body; it can shift from one side to the other; it can roll over completely; it can even turn somersaults. What is more, it can do all these things without even trying. Only Astronauts who have trained in gravity chambers to prepare for the experience of weightlessness, or who have actually been on space flights and space walks, can know the effortless freedom of life in the womb.

The fetus' practice movements make themselves known to the mother as little kicks and starts, shoves and gentle pangs. The mother may even be awakened at night by the vigor of its movements. She cannot feel the beat of her baby's heart, but the doctor can detect it. If she is carrying more than one child, he may have clues to this fact.

The chances of having twins are complicated to compute. Fraternal twins are much more common than identical twins. The reason is simple: identical twins come from a single fertilized egg that divides into two to produce two distinct individuals with the same genetic endowment. This is a rare occurrence. More often two eggs are released from the ovaries simultaneously and each is fertilized by a different sperm, with the result that fraternal twins are produced.

A number of factors have been discovered that increase the likelihood that a woman will bear fraternal twins. Age is a major determinant. A woman in her late thirties is more likely to give birth to twins than one who is still in her teens. Prior experience of motherhood also seems to increase the possibility of having twins.

American girls from 15 to 19 who have never had babies before have one chance in 200 of giving birth to twins. With women of 35 to 39 who have already borne a number of children, the chances go up to one in 50.

Science has not yet been able to determine why age should so greatly raise the likelihood that a woman will bear twins. It has been suggested that hormonal changes may develop in older women that make the cycles of ovulation less regular and predictable. During one month, an older woman may not ovulate at all, while during the next, two ova may be released into the Fallopian tubes. Such hormonal changes may also be induced by the drugs used to treat infertility and women taking such drugs are prone to multiple births.

Genetic characteristics, both familial and racial, play an important part in producing multiple births. Twinning seems to run in females of the same family, being passed on from mother to daughter.

One other fact is known with certainty about twins. They are more likely than other children to be born prematurely. On the average, twins arrive three weeks early. Twin births are therefore more precarious than single ones; the risk of mortality in the earliest days is theoretically more than four times as great. Actually, however, the outlook for premature twins is generally better than that for other premature babies.

The measure of maturity

The statistical criterion for prematurity is not the length of the mother's pregnancy but the baby's weight at birth. Any infant weighing less than five and a half pounds is considered premature. The reason for this method of calculating stems from the fact that the baby's weight can be determined with precision, whereas the duration of the mother's pregnancy cannot. Moreover, the weight of a single fetus is closely linked

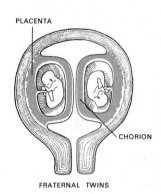

PLACENTA

CHORION

FRATERNAL TWINS

FRATERNAL TWINS, by far the more common of the two types of human twinning, are produced by fertilization of two different ova which arrive in the Fallopian tubes at approximately the same time. Genetically different, they are contained within separate chorionic sacs in the womb and are sustained by separate placentas.

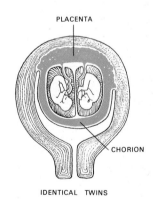

PLACENTA

CHORION

IDENTICAL TWINS

IDENTICAL TWINS result when the embryonic material growing from a single fertilized ovum separates into two distinct masses. The twins are genetic copies of each other and thus must be of the same sex. In most cases, they share one placenta, though they have separate umbilical cords. Siamese twins are born when separation is incomplete.

with its level of development: the longer it has had to grow, the larger it will be. But this rule does not hold for twins. Their weight and size are very much influenced by the fact that two are occupying space meant to hold one. Even if they are carried a full 40 weeks to term, they are usually smaller than single babies, although they are just as fully developed. And when the survival chances of twins weighing under five and a half pounds are compared with those of single infants of the same weight, the twins have a decided advantage because they are more fully developed at that weight.

Rescue by incubator

Prematurity can be ascribed to a number of causes, which may be linked to the mother's health or to the uterine environment. A chronic disease or an acute infection of the mother's body may bring on birth before term. Prematurity may be caused if the placenta separates from the uterine wall, or if the membranes around the fetus tear. Any of these conditions or accidents can bring on labor, and once labor begins, little can be done to stop it. In many cases, the baby is then doomed.

Prematurity is the most common cause of infant mortality in the United States, accounting for approximately 50 per cent of all newborn deaths. Even so, the modern incubator saves many. Essentially, the incubator is an artificial womb: its warm, moist, sterile atmosphere duplicates as much as possible the protection provided in uterine life. One of the spectacular saves in history was recorded in 1936. On January 14 of that year Jacqueline Benson was born at St. Anne's Hospital in Chicago, weighing only 12 ounces—a mere three quarters of a pound. After four and a half months in the incubator she was able to leave the hospital and she went on to grow to normal womanhood.

The smallest premature known to have survived, Jacqueline was probably born in the sixth month of her mother's pregnancy. And the six-month baby, even when it weighs considerably more than she did, has practically no chance of survival. It has to contend with the circulatory and respiratory difficulties that are created by incompletely developed body structures and an immature nervous system.

By the sixth month, however, many organs are virtually completely developed. The nostrils have opened, the eyebrows have begun to appear, and the ears are so fully developed that doctors have discovered babies in the womb can be startled by loud noises. And although the mother cannot hear the beat of her baby's heart, the baby may be able to hear the beat of hers. If he does, this steady, soothing rhythm would be part of his experience of life from the moment the sense of hearing begins to function. It may even play a role in development and growth.

An interesting experiment in this area has been conducted by Lee Salk with the cooperation of officials at Elmhurst Hospital in New York City. If further work bears out Dr. Salk's findings, change may be expected in the routine hospital care of newborn babies. Dr. Salk installed two loudspeaker systems in the nursery where newborn infants are kept for four days. Through these speakers he broadcast for 24 hours a day the beat of the normal human heart, 72 times a minute, at a moderate volume. When the babies who were exposed to the heartbeats were compared with others who were not, some extraordinary results were recorded. Among the babies in the first group, 69 per cent gained weight during their four days in the nursery, while 67 per cent of the babies in the second group gained no weight. Most of them, in fact, lost an average of 20 grams. Moreover, the first group of infants cried less, and breathed more deeply and regularly than the others, a fact to which Dr. Salk attributed their gain in weight. They put their energy into growing instead of dissipating it in tears and yells.

It is probably no accident that mothers—whether right- or left-handed —tend instinctively to hold their infants on the left side of the body, rather than the right. In this position, the baby can more easily hear the beat of its mother's heart.

After 40 weeks in the womb, the baby is ready for birth. The mother, too, is ready to give him up. The elastic walls of the uterus have stretched to capacity. Now the contractions begin that will push the baby out. These rhythmic movements, which make themselves known as labor pains, have an enormous force behind them. The uterus is the largest and most powerful muscle of the human body, stronger by far than a boxer's biceps. Even at the very beginning of labor, the contractions put 25 to 30 pounds of pressure on the contents of the womb.

A timetable for delivery

The first necessity in labor is to force open the cervix, the neck of the womb, so that the baby can enter the birth canal. This takes much longer than either of the next two stages of birth, which are the actual expulsion of the baby, followed by delivery of the placenta. Throughout the mother's pregnancy, the cervix has been virtually closed. It must be opened to a diameter of about four inches if the baby's head is to be able to pass through. The uterine contractions of the first stage of labor put so much pressure on the cervix that finally it dilates sufficiently.

Although the birth canal, like the uterus, is elastic enough to stretch, the baby's head always forces it. Indeed, in the process of birth the head is pressed somewhat out of shape. But this produces no damage. The bones of the baby's skull have not yet knit together. They are separated by sutures, and although they are pushed together as the baby traverses the narrow birth canal, they are never crushed. The head regains its

BRAIN DEVELOPMENT in the fetus is far enough along by the fourth month *(left)* that three major regions of the brain—the medulla, cerebellum and cerebrum—are clearly separate. By the sixth month *(middle)* a dentlike fissure appears on the surface of the cerebrum which will mark the border between the centers of sensation and voluntary muscular control. As the cerebrum expands, its surface, or cortex—the seat of higher mental processes—folds into many other fissures, thereby greatly increasing its area with a minimal increase in total brain volume.

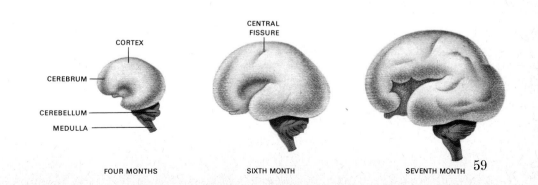

FOUR MONTHS   SIXTH MONTH   SEVENTH MONTH

normal shape a few days after birth. It takes longer for the skull bones to knit together; the soft spot at the top of a baby's head may not disappear until the child is more than a year old.

Until the moment of birth the mother has done everything for her child. She has provided him with food, protection, warmth and a nest in which to grow and develop. She has even breathed for him. In the placenta, oxygen from her bloodstream has been transferred to his. The fetus therefore has no need to breathe, although it does make practice movements with its breathing muscles. But if the baby does not breathe air once he is born, nine months of growth will have been to no avail. Moreover, he must take his first breath fairly quickly. We do not yet know precisely how long an infant can survive outside the womb without breathing. If the mother dies before the baby is born, it is possible for the baby to remain alive in the womb as long as 20 minutes. But this figure is somewhat misleading, for until the umbilical cord is cut, the placenta may still contain some oxygen. An adult will suffocate and die after only a few minutes without air. And this is probably the limit for an infant's survival after birth, too.

What impels the baby to take that vital first breath? Until recently the shock of birth seemed the only explanation. Everyone gasps on stepping into a cold shower or plunging into the icy ocean for a swim. It is possible that the newborn experiences birth in much the same way. Ejected forcibly from the warm world of the womb into the cold, he gasps. And in that first gasp and cry of protest he helps assure his survival. The attending physician's traditional slap on the upended baby's bottom provides another kind of shock, brought into use when the shock of birth does not force the first breath. Other factors are also at work. As anyone knows who has watched a litter of kittens or puppies being born, a newborn will sometimes lie still, unbreathing, for quite a while, and then suddenly "come to" with a sharp intake of breath. Shock cannot explain this response. It is likely that the breathing muscles are triggered into action by chemical changes within the body and changes of pressure in the chest cavity.

The first breath

According to Stanley James of Babies Hospital in New York City, these pressure changes may play a major part in causing the infant to take his first breath. While the baby is still in the womb, his lungs are crumpled up and deflated, although they contain some fluid. When the baby passes through the birth canal, his chest cavity is subjected to considerable pressure. This forces the fluid out through the nostrils and mouth. Immediately after birth, when the constriction has been removed, the chest expands the way a sponge does after being squeezed,

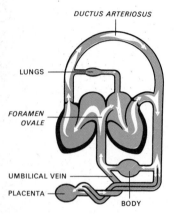

FETAL CIRCULATION is structurally quite different from postnatal circulation, because life-giving oxygen is delivered by the placenta, rather than the lungs. Most of the blood is diverted from the lungs by a special vessel, the *ductus arteriosus*, and a temporary hole between the right and left chambers of the heart, the *foramen ovale*.

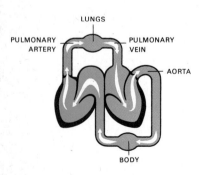

POSTNATAL CIRCULATION begins when the umbilical cord is clamped and the baby takes its first breath. The pulmonary arteries expand at this moment. As blood rushes into the lungs, muscles in the wall of the *ductus arteriosus* contract and close off the vessel. Pressure rises in the left chamber of the heart and the *foramen ovale* shuts permanently.

and air rushes into the lungs to fill the vacuum. The baby's first sound may not be the traditional cry, but a cough, designed to expel the last remaining fluid in the lungs.

If Dr. James is correct, the baby's first intake of air is a passive process. Thereafter, he must actively breathe for himself. And the effort this involves is sometimes Herculean. The first independent breath may take as much as 10 times the inhalation force required of an adult. The first few breaths expand the baby's lungs up to three quarters of their total capacity, but the healthy newborn does not seem to find this too much of a strain. His lungs expand this much every time he cries in anger.

Closing a valve

The circulatory system must also undergo dramatic changes if the baby is to survive. While the baby is still in the womb and its lungs are idle, relatively little blood circulates through their capillaries. The major route of circulation runs directly through the heart. Blood enters the upper right chamber, the right atrium, and passes from it to the upper left chamber, the left atrium, through an opening called the *foramen ovale,* or the oval window. When the blood has reached the left atrium, it is pumped into the lower left chamber, the left ventricle, and from there it moves into the aorta to begin its circulatory path. In order to prevent the blood from seeping back from the left atrium to the right, a flap descends over the *foramen ovale* after the blood has moved out of the right atrium.

After birth, the circulation route is completely different. Now all the blood must be sent to the lungs for purification and oxygenation. The venous blood, containing the waste products of metabolism, enters the right atrium, is squeezed into the right ventricle, and from there is sent via the pulmonary artery to the lungs. From the lungs, the oxygenated blood is returned to the left atrium, pumped into the left ventricle, and sent out through the aorta to begin circulating through the body.

Only 10 per cent of the fetus' blood is sent to the lungs; 55 per cent is returned to the placenta for oxygenation and 35 per cent is circulated through the blood vessels. The small amount of blood that does pass through the lungs makes its way there from the right side of the heart. While most of the blood in the right atrium is passed over to the left, some of it is squeezed into the right ventricle, and part of this blood is pumped out to the lungs. But more is present than the 10 per cent that the lungs can handle. In order to assure that the lungs are not burdened with more than their proper share, the embryo constructs a shunt, a tubular vessel known as the *ductus arteriosus.* The *ductus,* which begins to form in about the fifth week of uterine life, leads from the pulmonary artery to the aorta, and through it the right ventricle pumps all the blood which is not sent to the lungs.

The changeover from fetal to normal circulation thus requires an enormous alteration not merely in the functioning of the heart but also in its structure. The *foramen ovale* must be permanently sealed to keep the venous and arterial blood from mixing. For the same reason, the *ductus arteriosus* must constrict. Both processes begin with the first breath. The flap that seals the *foramen ovale* comes down, permanently, and in time adheres to the muscular wall that separates the right atrium from the left. The *ductus arteriosus* actively constricts; in 24 hours it has shut down and by the time the baby is two months old, it has become a fibrous cord. If, through some slipup, these events do not occur and the venous and arterial bloodstreams mix, the body may not receive enough oxygen. Surgery can now be called upon to repair nature's lapses in this regard by sealing off the *foramen ovale* or the *ductus*. The pioneer in this field was Dr. Robert E. Gross of Children's Hospital Medical Center, Boston. On August 26, 1938, Dr. Gross cut the open *ductus arteriosus* in the body of seven-year-old Lorraine Sweeney and then tied off both its ends, thus making her circulation normal.

The baby's first breath and the changes in his heart and circulatory system are the climax to nine months of growth in the womb. Not until he reaches puberty will comparably dramatic changes occur.

Early Scenes in a Human Life

The metamorphosis of a cell into a human being is no longer the mystery it was two decades ago, but scientists never see it happening. The process takes place in the privacy of a mother's womb. With the aim of visualizing it as nearly as possible, Swedish photographer Lennart Nilsson began seven years ago to photograph stages of embryonic growth in Stockholm hospitals where the embryos were removed for various medical reasons. The pictures on the following pages are part of his remarkable record. They show prenatal life in a form that to doctors is as fascinating as pictures of the far side of the moon. They depict, as a gynecologist put it, "living tissue in the living state." The circulation of blood, the first fetal movements and many other esoteric matters are seen more clearly than ever before. When Nilsson's project is finished, science will have a superb record of a process that has hitherto been inferred from circumstantial evidence.

THE BEGINNING OF FORM
Floating in a fluid-filled sac called the amnion, the 10-week-old fetus is a recognizable, if rudimentary, human. It measures about two inches from crown to rump. The fringed tissue seen at the right is the placenta, through which, via the arteries and vein of the umbilical cord, the fetus receives the oxygen and food products it requires from the mother and discards its wastes.

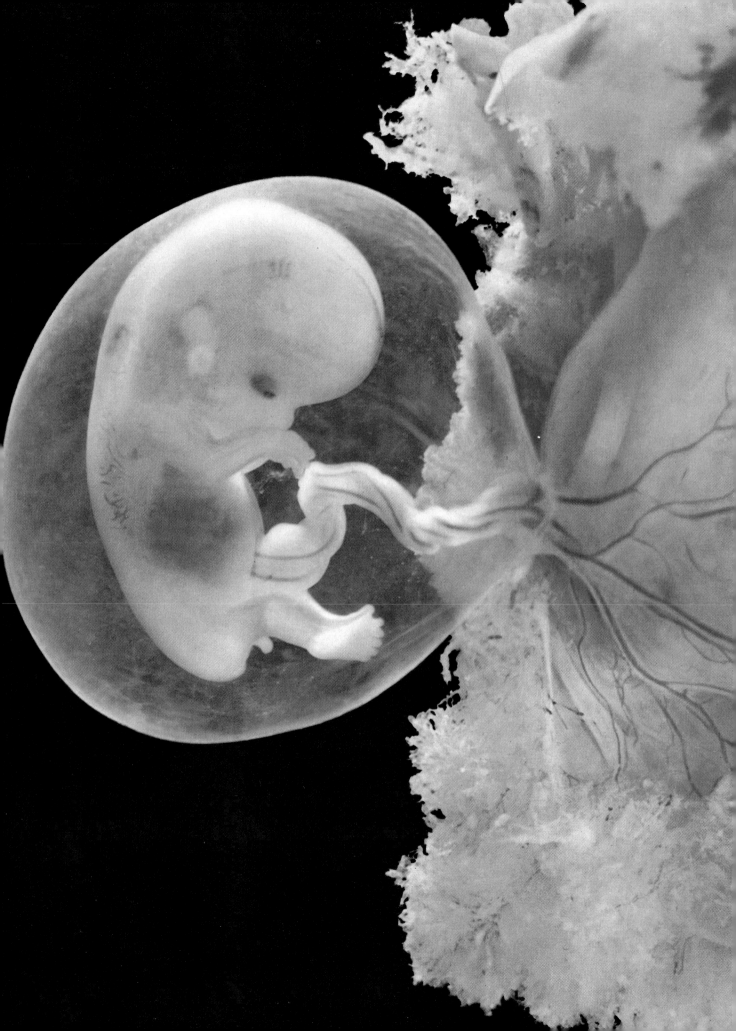

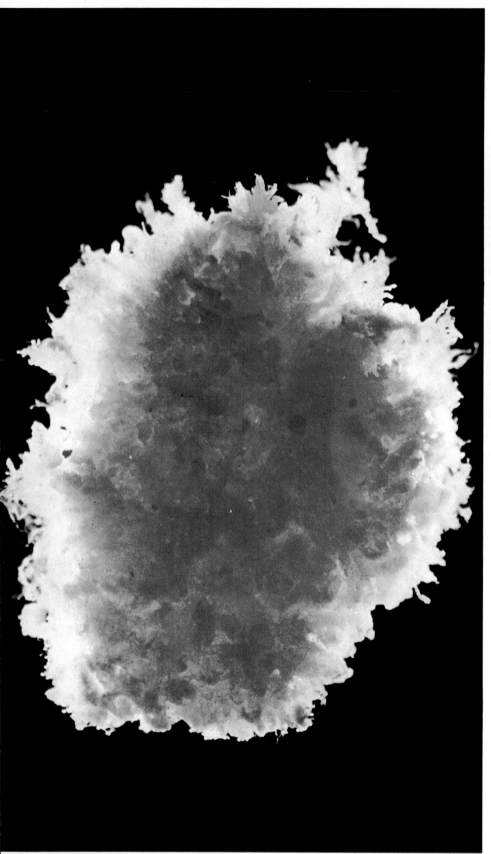

FOUR WEEKS OLD, the embryo *(left)* nestles inside a mass of feathery tissue called the chorion, which in turn is implanted in the uterus, cocklebur-fashion. The embryo draws nutrients from its mother through outgrowths, called villi, which help form the placenta.

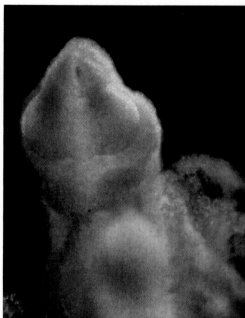

A SERIES OF BULGES, at 26 days, marks the areas of head and heart. The swellings at the top will become the forebrain; the smaller ones beneath them that look like cheeks are actually the lower jaw. The depression between these two sets of bulges will become the mouth. At the very top, a tiny hole is the end of a tube that forms the brain and spinal cord. Below the head, on the right, is another bulge containing the heart, where the first heartbeats have begun.

EYES, EARS AND LIMBS have appeared *(opposite)* by the sixth week, the latter as arm and leg "buds." The eye looks like a dark-rimmed circle; just in front of it is a bulge, part of which will form the nose. The series of little folds that look like a mouth are actually the beginnings of the outer ear. These features, which now seem out of place, will take their correct position when the embryo acquires a neck and begins to uncurl. The embryo is about an inch from crown to rump.

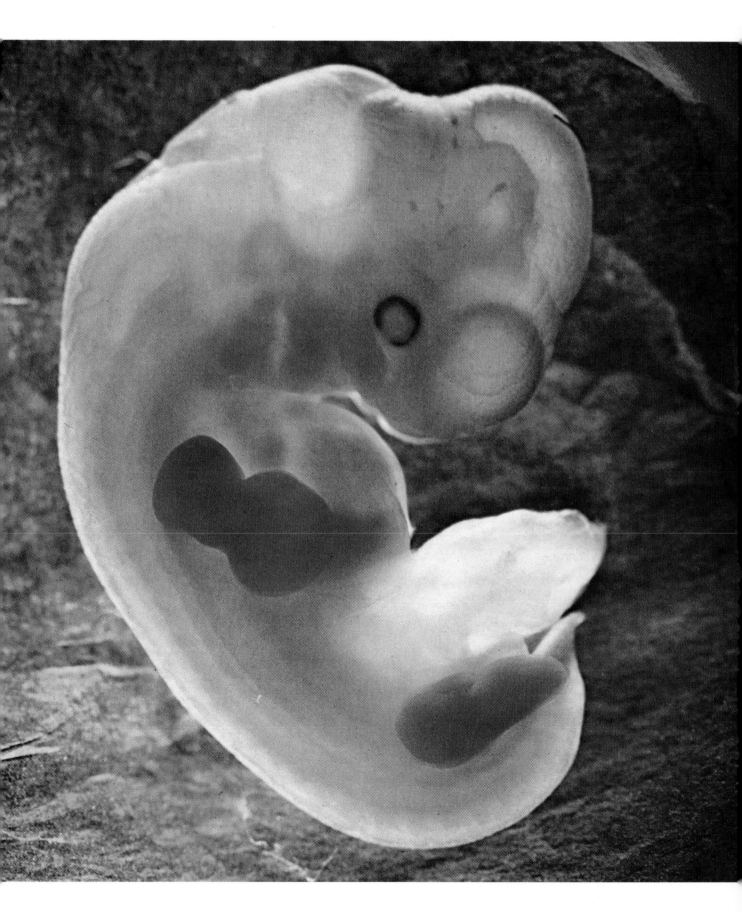

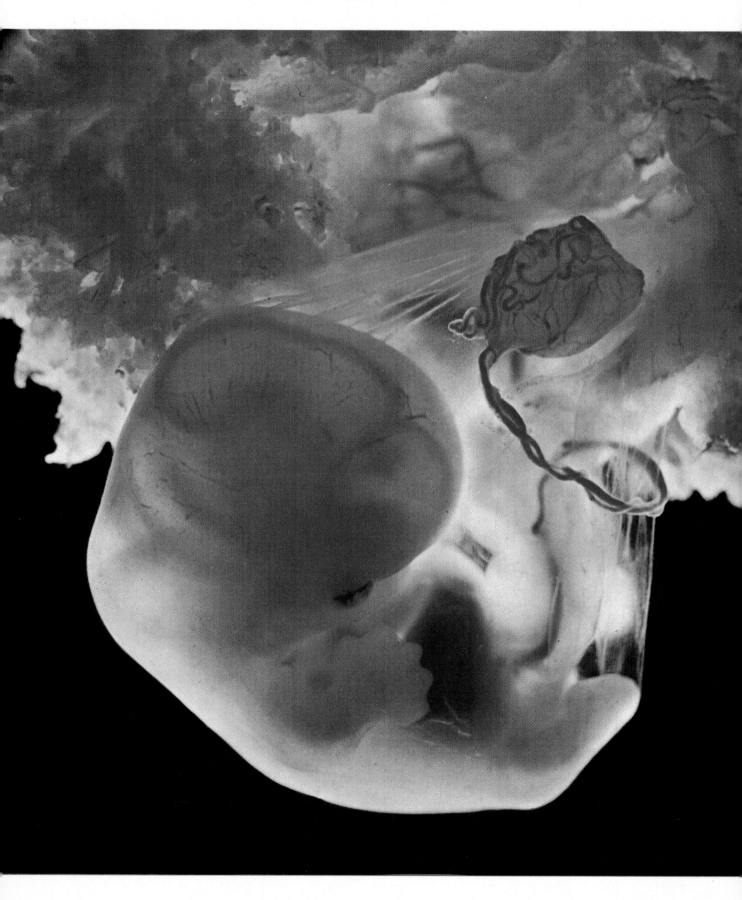

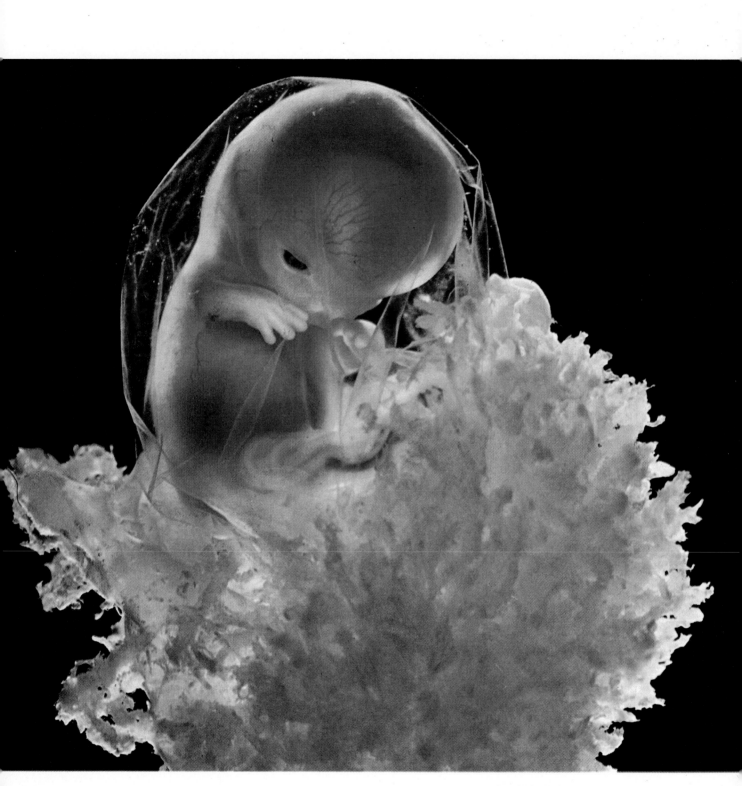

NINE WEEKS OLD, the embryo has developed well-formed fingers; its eye is assuming an oval shape. The embryo now measures about 1 1/4 inches from crown to rump. The kidneys have begun functioning at this stage, adding fetal urine to amniotic fluid.

THE YOLK SAC, prominent in this picture of an embryo at six weeks *(opposite),* produces red blood cells in the first two months of growth, but soon loses this function. It is rarely present at birth. Beneath the head, the arm can be seen with its developing hand.

AN EYELID FORMS
... AND CLOSES

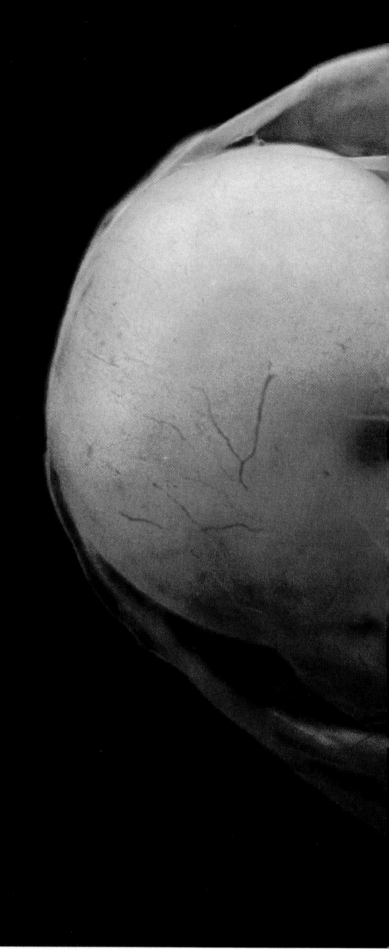

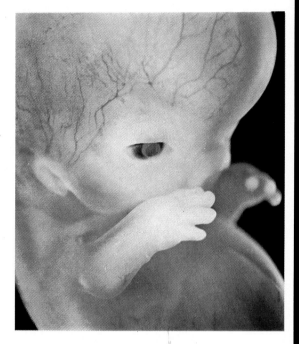

THE FACE of an eight-week-old embryo
(above) reveals an eyelid forming over the lens,
and the iris beginning to develop pigment.
In the ninth week, the upper and lower lids
meet, fuse, and do not reopen until the seventh
month. The ear can be seen at the left.

BY THE THIRD MONTH the developing form
of life is not just a human but an individual,
and has begun to show signs of distinctive
physical characteristics. No longer called
an embryo, it is now a fetus. During this month
it may double in length; here, the fetus
measures about 2¹/₂ inches from crown to rump.
Growth proceeds from the head down; the
feet, which lagged behind the hands in
development, have acquired fanned-out toes.

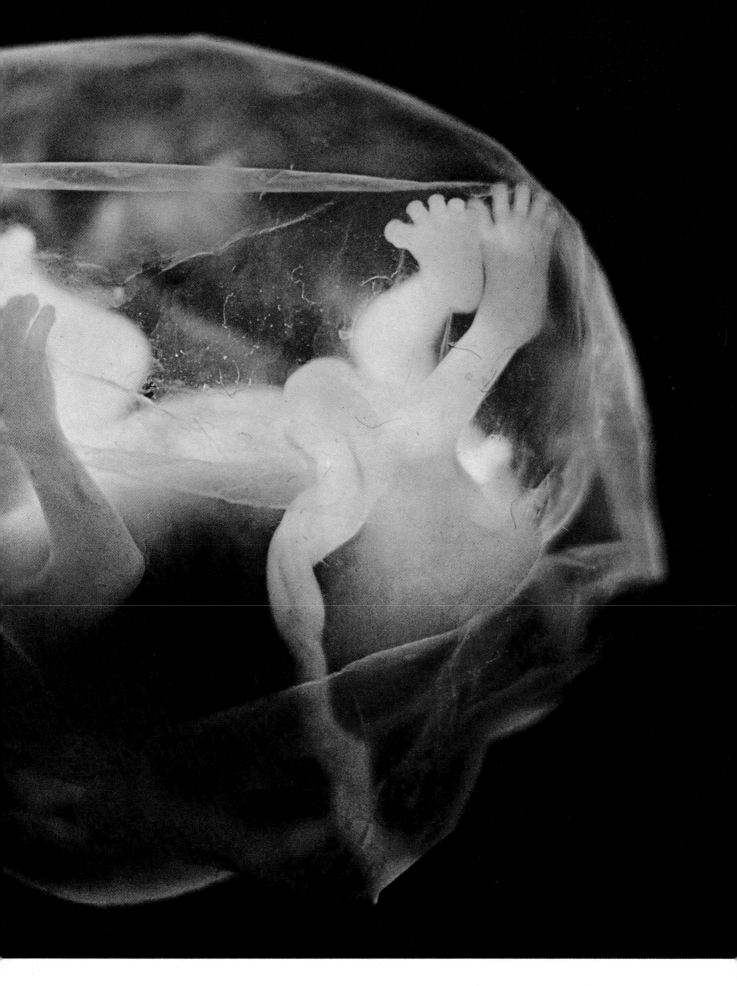

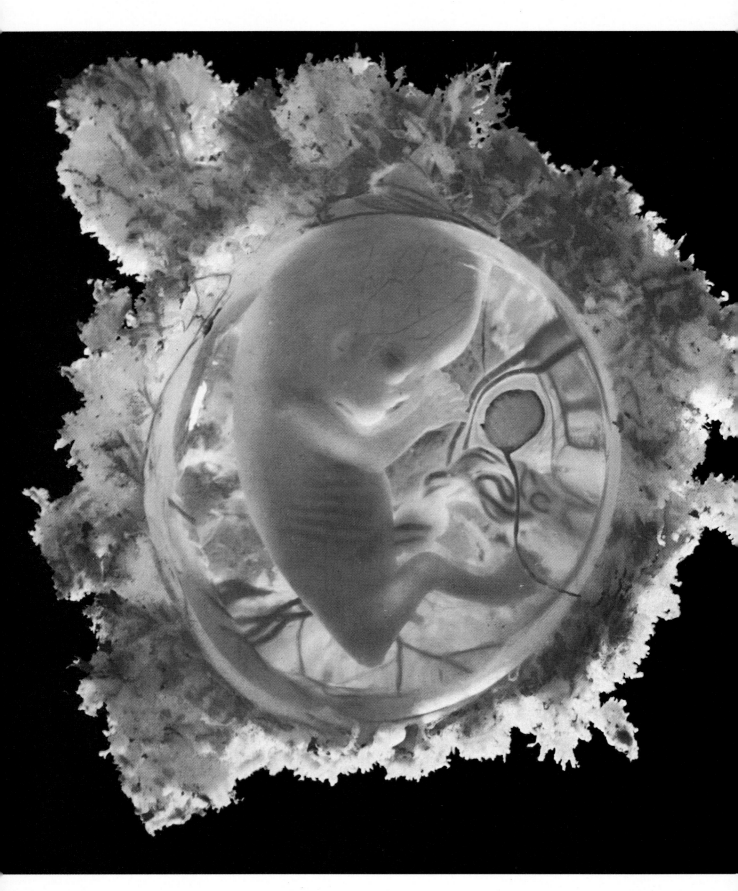

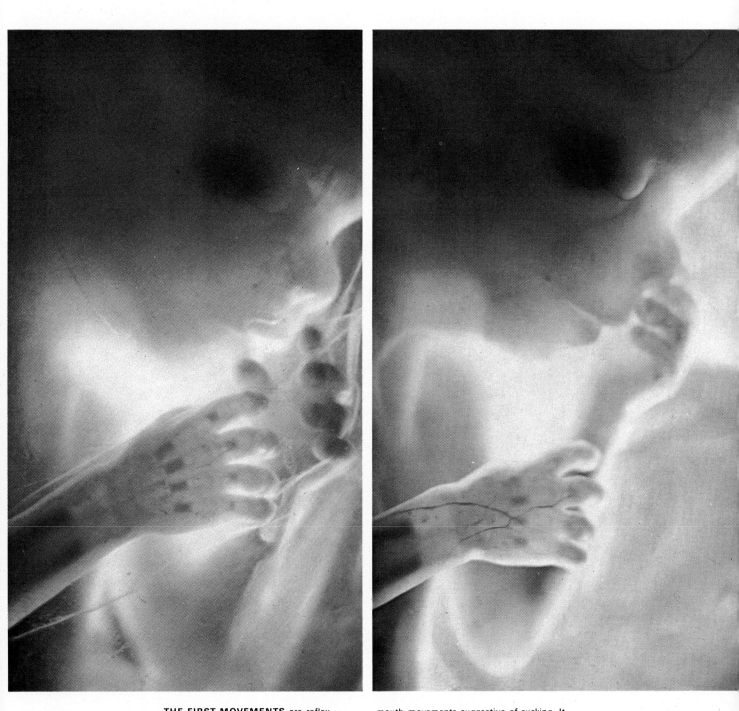

THE FIRST MOVEMENTS are reflex gestures, shown above in two pictures taken only seconds apart. Here, 12 weeks old, the fetus raises its hand to its mouth and makes mouth movements suggestive of sucking. It also contracts the other hand. The substitution of bone for cartilage in the long bones of the arms and legs is now well under way.

THE RIB CAGE of an 11-week fetus *(opposite)* can be seen in the chest region just below the elbows. The ribs and spinal column develop from cartilage cells, which begin to be replaced by bone cells at about the ninth week. Each rib grows out of a vertebra, but eventually a flexible joint will develop between the two.

FIFTH TO SIXTH MONTH: ACTIVITIES MULTIPLY

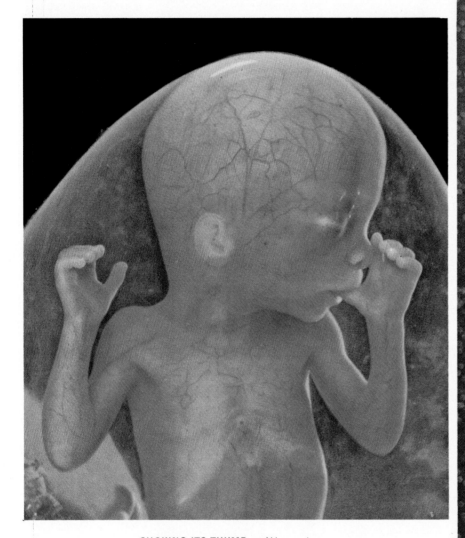

SUCKING ITS THUMB at 4½ months
(above), the fetus foreshadows the motions of
nursing. Some babies are born with thumb
calluses from too much sucking in the womb.
The fetus' movements intensify and are felt by
the mother as "quickenings"; a series of
rhythmic jolts means baby is hiccuping.
Nearly six inches from crown to rump, it has
almost fully developed ears and eyes. The
blood vessels show through its translucent skin.

FLOATING IN ITS SAC, the five-month fetus
has settled into a favorite "lie," or resting
position (each fetus picks its own). The
umbilical cord is kept from getting kinked
by the pressure of blood flowing through it.

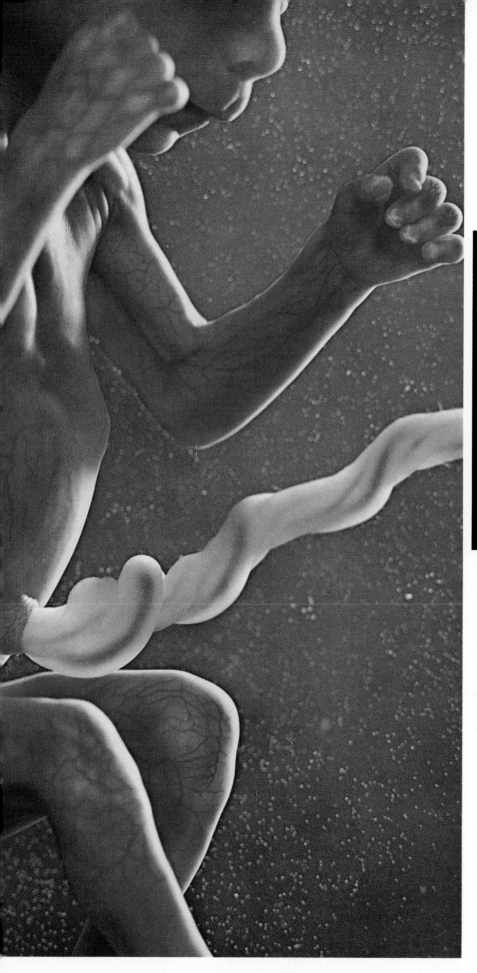

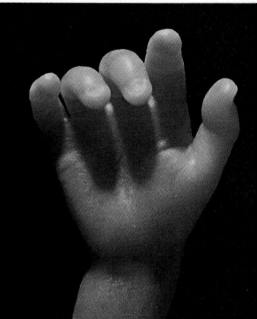

CURLING ITS FINGERS, a six-month-old fetus reveals emerging fingernails; by birth they will have grown long enough to need trimming. The fingerprints, which will forever mark it as unique, also begin to appear. The skin on its hands and feet has begun to thicken, in preparation for the wear and tear of postnatal life. At this stage the baby's grip is strong enough to hang on to anything within its reach. In fact, for reasons that embryologists do not fully understand, a fetus' grip in its sixth month is stronger than it is after birth. The waxy appearance of the hand comes from a protective film secreted by the skin.

IN THE LAST TWO MONTHS

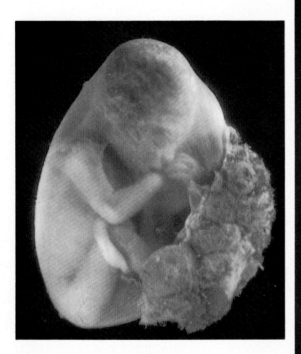

SEVEN MONTHS OLD, the fetus has acquired certain immunities and accumulated fat for warmth in preparation for the outer world. By now its digestive and respiratory systems have also become remarkably efficient. Born prematurely at this age, however, a baby can survive only with careful tending.

FULL-BORN AT NINE MONTHS, a baby emits a cry of life on being thrust into a cold, bright world. Gone is the dark warmth of the mother's womb; the umbilical cord is severed and closed off with a surgical clamp. Oxygen, which only moments before came from the placenta, is now supplied by the baby's own lungs. No one quite knows what makes breathing start. One theory is that when the fluid in the fetal lungs is forced out in the process of birth, a vacuum is created that causes the baby to inhale its first breath. From then on, the baby is on its own.

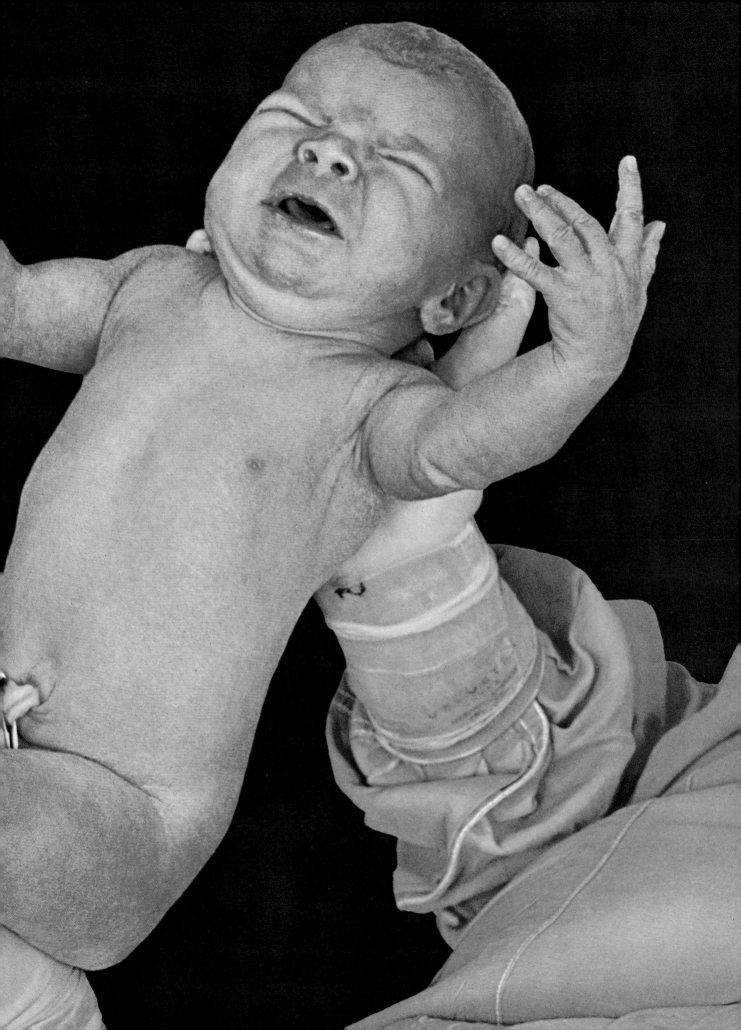

4
Some Yardsticks of Growth

ON APRIL 11, 1759, a French gentleman, Philibert Gueneau de Montbeillard, became the father of a son. De Montbeillard was a talented amateur scientist who had contributed to the immense encyclopedia of natural history compiled by his friend, Count Buffon. In the interests of science he measured the baby's length at birth and for the next 18 years he continued this practice, checking his son's height every six months or so. From these measurements he derived a table showing the height the boy had gained during each six-month interval—showing, in other words, the youngster's rate of growth, from infancy to adulthood.

The table indicated that this rate was not uniform from year to year. Each year the boy was taller than he had been the year before, but he grew less during his second year than during his first, and still less during the third than during the second. From his fourth to his eighth year he continued to grow at about the same rate. Then his speed of growth dropped again. At 11½, however, he began to shoot up, and for the next three and a half years he grew more each year. At 15, his growth curve slacked off for the last time. From then on he continued to grow less every year.

When De Montbeillard showed these figures to Buffon, the great naturalist decided to include them in a supplement to his encyclopedia. De Montbeillard's table was to become famous as the first longitudinal study of growth—the first examination of a child's pattern of growth over a period of time.

More than 100 years elapsed before any other scientist got around to following up the lead that De Montbeillard had provided. Thereafter a host of longitudinal growth studies proved that his observations were sound. Science now knows that all children grow in much the same way: rapidly at first, then more slowly, but very quickly indeed when puberty arrives. The same studies have shown that this general pattern leaves room for considerable individual variation: in the child's overall speed of growth, in the ages at which he grows most rapidly, and in the trajectory he follows to reach his destined height. These investigations have given rise to new methods of measuring growth and assaying a child's progress toward maturity. They have also shown that the child who is ahead of or behind his contemporaries, physically or mentally, will not necessarily remain in that position. And finally they have revealed that in many areas of the world children are growing larger and maturing earlier than they did a century ago.

The first scientifically based, large-scale longitudinal studies of growth in the United States were undertaken by the anthropologist Franz Boas. One of the towering figures in the field, Boas got into it by an indirect route. After studying physics and mathematics in his native Germany, he became interested in geography. In 1883, at the age of 25, he set off

INFANT TO YOUNG LADY
The snapshot history of one child records human growth from infancy to adolescence. Grace Osgood was eight weeks old in the first picture; the others were taken at yearly intervals. At six *(second row, second from right)* she no longer looks like a baby, and at 13 *(bottom row, second from left)*, at the peak of the adolescent growth spurt, she is suddenly a young lady.

for Greenland to study its landforms. He never got there. Stopping off on Baffin Island, he became fascinated by the local Eskimos. A year with them convinced him that his real vocation was here, the study of man.

Tradition has it that Boas' academic career in the United States had an equally unorthodox beginning. In 1888, a year after he had emigrated, he was on his way to a meeting of the American Association for the Advancement of Science. On the train he fell into conversation with G. Stanley Hall, a psychologist who had just been named President of Clark University in Worcester, Massachusetts. Hall was so impressed with his traveling companion that before the trip was over he had offered the young man a position as head of the anthropology department at Clark. There, in 1891, Boas began his pioneering study of growth.

Measurements that mislead

Scientific growth studies were not entirely unknown when Boas began his research, but until then the subject had been investigated almost exclusively through so-called cross-sectional studies: one-time measurements of large numbers of children of the same age. Cross-sectional studies are inexpensive and can be carried out quickly and easily, and they are an excellent means of establishing standards of height and weight at various ages against which to measure the individual child. However, as Boas recognized, they have a serious limitation. Because they deal only with averages, they offer no information at all about the growth pattern of any individual child. They show where he stands in relation to his contemporaries, but they do not show how far along he is in his own program of development. They can even lead to serious scientific error.

While Boas was still at work on his study, another investigator, Dr. William Townsend Porter, reported on a cross-sectional study of St. Louis schoolchildren. This indicated that youngsters who were advanced in their schoolwork were taller and heavier than children of the same age who were in lower grades. From these figures, Porter made a prediction for the future: because he assumed that all children grow at the same rate, he declared that those who were taller and brighter as children would invariably be taller and brighter when they became adults.

Although Boas' longitudinal study lasted only a year, it provided enough clues to persuade him that Porter was wrong. Boas' sample was made up of 100 Worcester schoolchildren—50 boys and 50 girls, ranging in age from five to 16 years old. At both the beginning and the end of the experimental year, he and his assistant took a number of measurements on each child: height, both standing and sitting; weight; length and breadth of head; length of forearm and breadth of hand. In analyz-

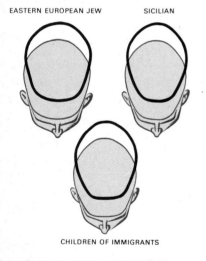

EASTERN EUROPEAN JEW   SICILIAN

CHILDREN OF IMMIGRANTS

A STUDY OF SKULL PATTERNS led to the discovery in 1912 that environment plays a role in shaping human heads. Previously, it had been assumed that the shapes of heads stayed extremely constant within races and ethnic groups. Then the pioneering anthropologist Franz Boas measured the heads of 18,000 immigrants and first-generation children of immigrants. The study showed that American-born children *(bottom)* of Eastern European Jews *(upper left)* had longer heads than their round-headed parents, and the heads of the children of long-headed Sicilians *(upper right)* became shorter.

ing the data, Boas took account of each youngster's height in relation to the average for his age and sex. From all these statistics he was able to extract a number of conclusions. The children's speed of growth, he found, depended on their ages: the younger grew more slowly than those who had reached adolescence. Age was not the only factor. Each child seemed to have his own internal clock, regulating his journey to adulthood at its own speed. Among the younger children, the shorter ones grew more slowly, but among the adolescents, the pattern was reversed. The shorter ones grew more rapidly; in addition, they continued growing for a longer period of time.

Boas' most important discovery, and one which has been confirmed by every subsequent study, was that speed of growth is not decisive in fixing a child's final height. True, some slow-growing children never become tall. But others, simply by continuing to grow for a longer time, may end as adults of above-average height. And what is true of height is true of all other aspects of development. Every child grows at his own individual speed, some maturing early, others late. As Boas himself phrased it, in a paper published in the 1930s, "In some individuals the whole physiological development . . . proceeds rapidly and energetically and the whole development period is short; in others it is sluggish and occupies a much longer period."

Since this is the case, a child's chronological age cannot describe his progress very meaningfully, especially during puberty, when growth is rapid and so much change is going on. The statement that a boy is 14 does not tell whether he is in the middle of adolescence, has already passed it, or has not yet reached it. Because it says nothing at all about his level of maturity, it offers very little guidance to physicians, educators or parents—the people most intimately concerned with the youngster's growth. What they need to know is the point he has reached in his own development. His developmental age, as it is called, is far more important to them than his age in years.

Measuring by remembrance

The concept of developmental age was first put forth by Charles Ward Crampton, a New York physician and a collaborator of Boas. Crampton suggested that the appearance of pubic hair in boys and the onset of menstruation (the menarche) in girls be used as the base points of measurement. Developmental age would then be determined by counting backward or forward from this time. But it soon became evident that this information would not suffice. The accuracy of the method depended entirely on the accuracy of the child's memory, and although girls are likely to remember when they began to menstruate, boys are apt to be quite vague in their recollections of the date that pubic hair first appeared. To meet this objection, other criteria were gradually added: the appearance of pubic hair in girls and of axillary (armpit) hair in both sexes; the development of the sex organs; the emergence of the breasts in girls and of facial hair and the Adam's apple in boys. The degree of development of all these characteristics can be rated on a sliding scale, and by combining the ratings the physician can measure developmental age in the adolescent period.

This approach, based as it was on the outward signs of puberty, had a drawback: it was not satisfactory as a way of measuring developmental age during childhood. By offering a look backward from puberty, it could lead to inferences on where the child had been at various times in his earlier years. But it provided no way of measuring his developmental age in childhood or of determining his speed of growth.

Clues from X-rays

During the early years of the century, two investigators working independently found a method of assaying growth that works on children of any age. Using the then-new technique of X-ray photography, they discovered that the ossification of the hand and wrist bones varies considerably among children of the same age. All 29 bones in this area begin as bits of cartilage; gradually, in regular and predictable stages, they harden into bone. Once the sequence of these changes was carefully mapped, assigning a developmental age to any growing child became a relatively simple matter. An X-ray of the youngster's wrist, showing how far ossification had progressed, could be compared with a set of standard charts. The method is very useful, because neither the order of events nor the nature of the changes that occur is affected by the child's health or by any of the myriad of other processes that normally go on in his body, apart from diseases of the hand bones themselves.

Today, two other structures may also be X-rayed to find developmental age: the bones of the knee, and the teeth. For the period of infancy—between six months and two years—the milk teeth can be used, since they emerge and fall out in a fairly regular order; between six and 13 years, the equally regular appearance of the permanent teeth provides an index of growth.

Except for the teeth, which appear to develop on their own timetable, all these measurements agree quite closely among themselves in providing a determination of a child's developmental age. They also provide scientific confirmation of a fact suggested by everyday observation: girls move toward maturity more rapidly than boys. X-rays of both hand and knee show that girls are on the average about 20 per cent ahead of boys at any age up to physical maturity. Even the teeth reflect a difference. Though both sexes acquire their milk teeth at about the same age, per-

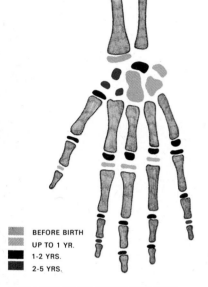

BEFORE BIRTH
UP TO 1 YR.
1-2 YRS.
2-5 YRS.

A CALENDAR OF DEVELOPMENT is provided by the hardening of cartilage into bone, because it proceeds by slow, predictable stages. The X-ray above shows the hand and wrist of a five-year-old boy, colored to indicate when various "ossification centers" hardened. X-rays of this kind are used to check developmental age against chronological age.

manent teeth appear earlier in girls—the molars by about two months and the canines by as much as 11.

In fact, girls seem to start out in life with certain advantages over boys. Until the age of five months, girls lead in the ability to perform the movements that are prerequisite for creeping, sitting and walking, and even after that age they generally remain ahead in acquiring skills that demand fine movements and motor coordination, such as tying bows or skipping. They usually learn to control their bladders somewhat earlier. In theory, this feminine advantage should result from a more rapid development of the brain, paralleling the faster skeletal development of girls. But no evidence of brain differences between the sexes has yet emerged, although the studies that have been conducted since the 1930s by Jesse L. Conel of Harvard University have thrown much light on the developmental processes in the cerebral cortex, the region of the brain that governs perception, thought and voluntary muscle control.

By mapping the patterns of growth in the cortex during the first two years of life, Conel has been able to show why the skills of both sexes emerge in the order that they do. By the time a baby is born, he has already developed all the brain cells he will ever have. Brain growth after birth consists primarily of an increase in the size of the cells and in the number and complexity of the axons and dendrites, the long, branching fibers that carry impulses from one cortex cell to another, enabling the cells to function together. These postnatal increases, Conel has found, occur first in the areas of the cortex that control movement, then in the sensory areas, beginning with those that govern the sense of touch. The vision and hearing areas develop somewhat later. However, these later-developing areas are already functional at birth. Experiments have shown that even a week-old baby can perceive simple differences in shapes, showing more interest in a pattern of concentric circles than in a triangle. But the ability to perceive more complex patterns—and this includes people—develops later: it takes several months for even a wise child to know his own mother or father.

The development of coordination

Conel has also found sequential priorities in growth even within particular areas of the cortex. For example, the motor cells that control the muscles of the upper arms develop interconnections before those that control the hands. (Any parent knows that a baby can flail its arms about long before it can control its fingers sufficiently to pick something up.) As the parts of the cortex continue to mature, all of the baby's responses to stimuli and all of his movements become more precise. By the time he is one and a half, he can learn to walk and feed himself, though sloppily. At two he can control his bowels and can begin to control his bladder.

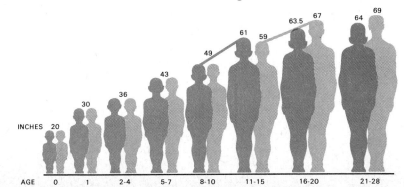

THE RACE FOR MATURITY between the sexes is seen in this chart comparing heights and ages of growing boys and girls. Both sexes grow nearly evenly until an early adolescent growth spurt makes girls uncomfortably taller than boys. The boys gain the lead when a delayed but larger spurt carries them toward a final five-inch margin.

By this age, too, most children have begun to speak, displaying that form of behavior which is most distinctively human.

All these responses can be delayed by serious illness or by severe deprivation. But in a normal child, none of them can really be stopped. On the other hand, none of them can emerge before the brain has matured to an appropriate degree; throughout the growing years the child's behavior is heavily dependent on the development of his nervous system. For this reason specialists in development warn parents against attempting to impose behavior patterns, such as toilet training, on a child before his nervous system is mature enough to cope with them.

The adolescent spurt

It is at the beginning of adolescence, the years of greatest growth, that developmental differences between girls and boys become most evident. Girls generally reach puberty ahead of boys: they embark on the adolescent growth spurt at an average age of 10½, as against 12½ for boys. Although the intensity and duration of this spurt vary widely from one youngster to another, it usually lasts for two to two and a half years in both sexes. The growth and transformation that occur in this short period of time are enormous, second in magnitude only to those that take place in the womb: as nine months of pregnancy turn an egg into a human being, so the years of adolescence turn a child into an adult, capable of performing all the biological functions of maturity.

Though the growth spurt begins earlier in girls, it is during this period that boys outstrip them in development. In childhood, boys and girls of the same age are practically the same height. But the boy's spurt is markedly greater. While it is going on, the average boy grows approximately eight inches taller and adds 45 pounds to his weight; at its peak, about 14, he is growing at the rate of four inches a year. Girls gain about six and a quarter inches in height and 35 pounds in weight during the spurt. Their peak comes sooner, at about 12, when their rate of growth averages three and a quarter inches a year. The more powerful acceleration in boys is the main reason that men are, on the average, taller than women. A secondary reason is that the growth spurt comes later in boys, who can thus continue growing for a longer time.

Every muscular and skeletal dimension of the body seems to take part in the adolescent spurt. The growth of the heart, stomach and other visceral organs speeds up. The head, whose increase in size has been almost imperceptible since the child was eight, steps up its pace of growth slightly. Even the eyeballs expand in front-to-back measurement. Sometimes this increase is disproportionate, and leads to nearsightedness.

The contours of the face, which have been altering gradually throughout childhood, show particularly marked changes. The whole profile becomes more angular, the forehead more prominent, the chin more pointed, the nose longer. These changes, which are associated with the growth of facial bone, are accompanied by subtle changes in muscle size and in the distribution of fatty tissue under the skin, making the adolescent's facial expression so different from that of a child.

In both sexes, strength increases, although the increase is proportionately much greater in boys than in girls. Before puberty, most girls can hold their own in tussles with boys of the same age. But this is no longer so after the growth spurt. From then on, the male sex is truly the stronger one. To cite just one example: the average boy can exert more than 120 pounds of thrust with one arm, as against 70 pounds for girls.

Growth may continue, although slowly, for many years after adolescence. Some people are still growing—though almost imperceptibly—in their forties. For all practical purposes, however, growth ceases in the teens. On the average, boys reach 98 per cent of their final height by the time they are 17¾, girls by the time they are 16½.

These statistical and descriptive summaries of the adolescent spurt, like most summaries, oversimplify what is in fact a rather complicated process. Detailed studies have shown that the various parts of the body grow at different rates, as do various dimensions of each part. Moreover, each part, each dimension reaches its maximum rate of growth at a different time. But within this apparent chaos a definite order has been found. The feet speed up first, reaching their peak growth rate only about three months after the spurt has started. In another six months it is the turn of the calf and the thigh. Four months later the hips and chest begin broadening at an accelerated rate, followed by the shoulders. In both sexes, the length of the trunk and the depth of the chest reach peak growth speed last of all.

Man-sized body, boy-sized muscles

These patterns of acceleration pose temporary problems for many children. It seems to be true that a boy can, in a certain sense, "outgrow his strength." Strength increases during the growth spurt but sometimes more slowly, at first, than height and weight. Until his strength catches up with him, the youngster may have to operate a man-sized body with muscles that are not quite up to man-sized effort. Again, growing girls often worry about the size of their hands and feet, fearing that they will be ungainly all their lives. But since these extremities reach their maximum size long before the arms and legs, a young woman's proportions will almost certainly improve in time.

Measurements of all growth factors—from degree of bone ossification to overall body proportions—provide something more than a simple description of the child's level of development at any given time; they can predict his future as well. For example, in 1954 a 10-year-old girl applied for admission to the Royal Ballet School in England. Although she gave evidence of considerable talent as a dancer, the director was quite hesitant about accepting her application. She was small for her age, and he feared her height as an adult would be less than five foot two, the minimum for ballerinas in most professional companies. But the youngster was eager and persuasive, and the director finally agreed to consult a growth expert who might be able to forecast her final height. The expert compared such telltale factors as the rate of ossification of her wrist bones with the data he had laboriously collected for hundreds of children over a period of 15 years. From the comparison, he concluded that the girl had more growing ahead of her than the average child of her age, and that she would be about five foot three when she reached maturity. On the basis of this prediction, the girl was admitted to the school. She grew to five foot four, and after her graduation was accepted as a member of the corps de ballet of a major dance company.

The internal regulator

The concept of developmental age and the discovery of ways to determine it have added considerably to knowledge of the growth process. For example, science now knows that the internal clock which regulates each child's speed of growth is capable of making many adjustments for interference from environmental obstacles. Illness or poor diet may slow the clock temporarily, so that the child grows at a reduced rate for a while. However, if the interference does not last too long, the clock will eventually speed up, and the child may grow at double or even triple his normal rate until he makes up the lost time.

Differences in individual rates of growth can create social and psychological difficulties. The child who is ahead in physical development at an early stage of his life will have few such problems. This youngster is likely to remain ahead of his contemporaries throughout the growing years, despite temporary setbacks. Not so the child who develops slowly and late. Though he may eventually grow taller than the child who matures early, he may meanwhile be made miserable in any number of ways. In a society that tends to group children almost exclusively on the basis of their chronological age, the late maturer is constantly at a disadvantage. Not only is he smaller and lighter, he is, on the average, a little behind in the development of motor skills and intelligence. He may therefore do less well at schoolwork and athletics. As a result he may be put in a class with children a year or more younger than he is. Being "held back" may produce emotional problems that further affect his ability to learn. Trapped in a vicious circle, he may keep dropping behind, so that even when he finally catches up in size, he

PRECOCIOUS INTELLECTS, 17th Century French mathematician Blaise Pascal and German poet and playwright Wolfgang Goethe, are commemorated on these stamps. Both displayed astounding creative development at an early age. Pascal *(top)*, without any books or teacher, taught himself geometry before the age of 12. Goethe *(bottom)* wrote his first play when he was 10.

may be unable to catch up emotionally and intellectually.

Actually, a child's rate of development—physical or intellectual—is a totally inadequate clue to his final achievement. The life histories of any number of successful people make it clear that slow growth is not always an unmixed curse. Two of the greatest men of the 20th Century— Albert Einstein and Winston Churchill—were considered backward as children. Einstein was so late in learning to talk that his parents feared he was subnormal. He also appears to have been slow in overall physical development. As a man he was of medium height, with broad shoulders and a well-developed musculature. As a child he was small, slender and notably unathletic. He considered himself a weakling, and disliked such physical activity as running, jumping and playing games. Churchill, who was born prematurely at seven months, was always shorter than other boys his age. His father, his governess and most of his teachers were convinced he was dull and untalented. Sent to school when he was seven, he hated it from the beginning, was always at the bottom of his class and was "kept back" several times.

Although late intellectual flowering may simply reflect slow growth, precocious mental ability in young people often reflects something more than rapid growth. A favorable environment and parental encouragement may stimulate a youngster's intellectual development, but they are not enough to explain the feats that child prodigies have been known to achieve. The 19th Century British philosopher John Stuart Mill was the son of a brilliant man who was himself a philosopher of note. But the word "brilliant" does not begin to describe young John. He learned Greek at three, wrote a history of Rome when he was six and a half, was deep in the study of solid geometry when he was nine, and at 12 frequently debated philosophy as an equal with his father. Mozart, one of the greatest names in music, was himself the son of a musician. Both he and his sister were subjected to enormous pressure by their ambitious father. But these facts cannot account for the composer's early signs of genius. At three, Mozart could memorize musical passages simply by listening to them once. Before he was seven he was touring the courts of Europe, giving recitals on the violin and the clavier. Minuets he wrote when he was six are standard learning pieces for many beginning piano students, and he wrote his Fourteenth Symphony, which is still in the repertoire of most orchestras, when he was only 15 years old.

Brain, environment and intelligence

Precocity like this may in part reflect rapid growth, but it must also have something to do with particular characteristics of the brain, which result from some peculiarly favorable combination of heredity and environment. The nature of these characteristics is not known, although it is generally agreed that intelligence is related to the number and nature of the interconnections among the cells of the brain, and to the action of the various chemical substances it secretes. The development of intelligence, precocious or otherwise, is much influenced by the child's environment. Indeed, environmental changes are presumably responsible for an apparent rise in the general level of intelligence—at least as measured by I.Q. tests—among American children. The rise seems to have been going on since about 1916, when the tests were first put into common use. Some of the changes that have undoubtedly gone into producing it are better living conditions, including better nutrition; improved means of communication; improved methods of education; improved intelligence tests; even improved skill among children in taking the tests. However, the rise may also stem from another—and more mysterious—factor: a long-term—or in statistician's jargon, "secular"—trend, a decade-to-decade, generation-to-generation tendency of people to mature earlier and faster, and to grow bigger, taller and heavier.

The long-range trend

The oldest statistical evidence of such a trend dates back to the early 19th Century. For more than 200 years the Norwegian Government has kept records of the heights of all the young men who have served in that country's Army. These records show no appreciably average increase in height for the first 90 years. But in about 1830 the figures began to rise, and they have been rising consistently ever since. By 1875, the average Norwegian soldier was half an inch taller than his forebear of a half century before, and by 1935 he was an inch and a half taller still.

Virtually every country in the world seems to have been affected by the secular trend. It has been observed in Japan and in Argentina, in Estonia and in the United States. The changes associated with the secular-trend increase show themselves very early. Since the middle of the 19th Century, babies in many parts of the world have been increasing in size and weight at birth. Older children have also been growing bigger. Between 1880 and 1950, for example, the average height of American and Western European children between the ages of five and seven has increased more than half an inch every 10 years, for a total of more than four inches; the average height of adolescents has increased by seven inches. Records at Marlborough College in England indicate that between 1873 and 1943 the average height of its 16-year-old students increased more than half an inch every 10 years.

Adults have increased in height less spectacularly than adolescents: about four inches in America and Western Europe since the mid-19th Century. However, while children are growing faster, they also stop growing sooner. Early in the century, most men reached their final height at around 26 years; since then the age has dropped to 18 or 19.

Just as growth now ends earlier, so adolescence and its growth spurt now begin earlier. It is known that girls have been reaching the menarche at a younger age every generation since the early part of the 19th Century. Records from the industrial city of Manchester, England, show that in 1820 girls from the lower social and economic classes attained menarche at an average age of 15.7. "Educated ladies"—who benefited from adequate nutrition as well as a ladylike education—reached it at 14.6 years. A 1963 report gave the figure as a little over 13 years for the first group and a little under 13 for the second. In the United States, records kept since 1900 show that the age of menarche has been steadily dropping here too. In almost every country for which figures are available over the past century, the girls of each generation have been reaching puberty nearly 10 months earlier than their mothers. At the same time, the menopause has been arriving later, so that women's span of fertility has been increasing.

Obviously, such rapid and dramatic changes in height and rate of growth toward maturity cannot have been going on uninterruptedly since the human race first evolved. Indeed, there is considerable evidence that in both the ancient world and in medieval Europe puberty occurred at about the age of 14. The Jewish ritual that invests a boy with adult responsibility—the Bar Mitzvah—traditionally takes place when he is 13. Shakespeare's Juliet was 14, and all through the Middle Ages marriage at that age or even younger was common. Other evidence shows that the secular trend has at times been slowed down or even reversed. In the early 19th Century, when the Industrial Revolution was changing the face of the Western world, a significant retardation took place in height, weight and age of menarche. The babies born immediately after the Second World War in most parts of the world were smaller and lighter than were those born only a few years earlier.

Does bigger mean better?

The obvious explanation is that the secular trend is related to improvements in nutrition and in living conditions. But this does not seem to account for all the facts. The Industrial Revolution, with its introduction of child labor in the factories and mines, swept over Great Britain very quickly. It produced, at least at first, many deleterious changes in the average man's way of life. But the effect of these changes on growth seems to have been no more serious in Great Britain than in Scandinavia, where the pace of the Industrial Revolution was considerably slower and its impact more moderate. Similarly, all the countries that participated in the Second World War suffered a severe, although temporary, decline in their living standards. Yet in neutral Switzerland,

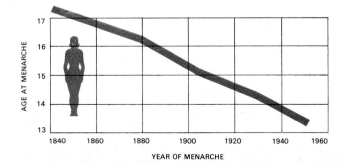

AGE AT MENARCHE

17

16

15

14

13

1840   1860   1880   1900   1920   1940   1960

YEAR OF MENARCHE

PUBERTY AGE IN NORWAY has been steadily declining, as shown in this chart, which gives the age at which girls in that country have been reaching the menarche, the time when menstruation begins. In the 1950s the age was about 13½—four years earlier than it was in 1840. According to one theory, the trend results from improved living standards. If it continues, the average girl may reach sexual maturity at 12 or even younger.

which enjoyed prosperity and a normal standard of living throughout the war years, the postwar crop of babies was also smaller and lighter.

Several other explanations for the secular trend have also been advanced—none of which, however, is really satisfactory. It has, for example, been attributed to a long-term rise in the world's temperature. Few scientists take this proposal very seriously. Studies of animals, indeed, suggest that a hot, moist climate may actually retard growth. Certain animals in cold climates average larger than closely related species in warmer areas. More mobile populations, resulting in intermarriage between genetically diversified people, has also been advanced as a reason for the trend. This may indeed be a factor that would explain part of the increase, but science does not yet have sufficiently detailed knowledge of the genetics of height to be able to endorse the suggestion completely.

The long-term effects of the secular increase are far from clear. Physically bigger does not necessarily mean better. Furthermore, the trend may be aggravating an already troublesome problem. Even as children reach puberty earlier, their attainment of economic independence is increasingly postponed, through the years demanded by college and professional study. The result is an incongruous prolongation of adolescence in a social sense long after it has been passed in physical reality.

Searching for the Secrets of Development

The largest, longest continuous study of human growth in America is being conducted at the Fels Research Institute for the Study of Human Development, located on the Antioch College campus in Yellow Springs, Ohio. There, since 1929, more than 600 individuals, ranging from yet-to-be-born babies to 80-year-olds, have been regularly measured and tested. They are studied weekly for six weeks before birth, twice a year from birth to their 18th year, and yearly thereafter. Fels scientists, seeking to define the basic principles of growth, often find that their data merely confirm popular knowledge. Example: tall parents do tend to have tall children. But there have been surprising new discoveries as well: clues about the personality of a child can be found in its behavior as a fetus; intelligence quotients, widely believed to yield unchanging results through a lifetime, can actually vary significantly from year to year.

SIZING UP THE SKULL
Jane Brucker, eight and a half, has her head clamped still for an X-ray which will record another step in the growth of her head bones and teeth. Her skull growth will be largely complete when she reaches 10, but her jawbone may continue growing for years afterward. Jane is one of some 460 children and adults whose physical growth is being measured regularly at the Institute.

FIGURES FOR THE FUTURE

Jane Brucker's height is measured *(right)* at four foot eight inches. From this figure plus her skeletal development (a half year ahead of average) plus the average height of her parents, Fels scientists are able to estimate that her final height at age 18 will be five foot nine inches.

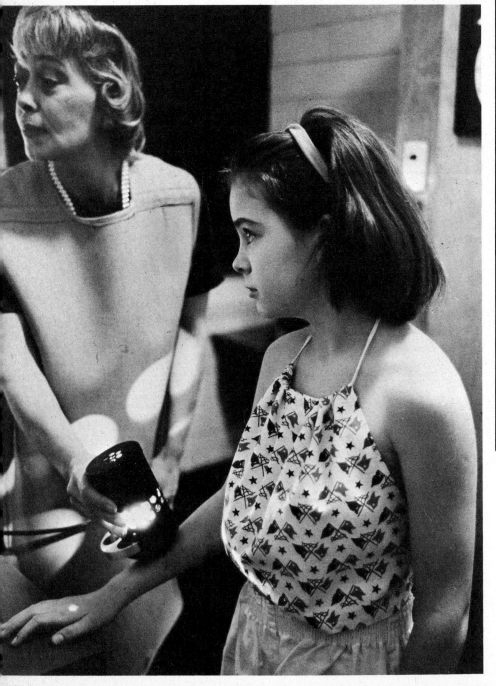

BIG FACTS IN LITTLE BONES

Regular X-rays of her hand, wrist and forearm *(above)* keep track of Jane's "skeletal age." The 29 bones in the hand and wrist ossify at different rates in different people. The rates can be compared with established averages to reveal whether growth is faster or slower than normal.

CASTING LIGHT ON DARKNESS

The darkness of Jane's skin is measured *(left)* by a light meter to show how pigment develops and how skin color is inherited. Fels investigations proved that the ability to tan is inherited separately from skin color: at the beach, a blonde may tan while a brunette burns.

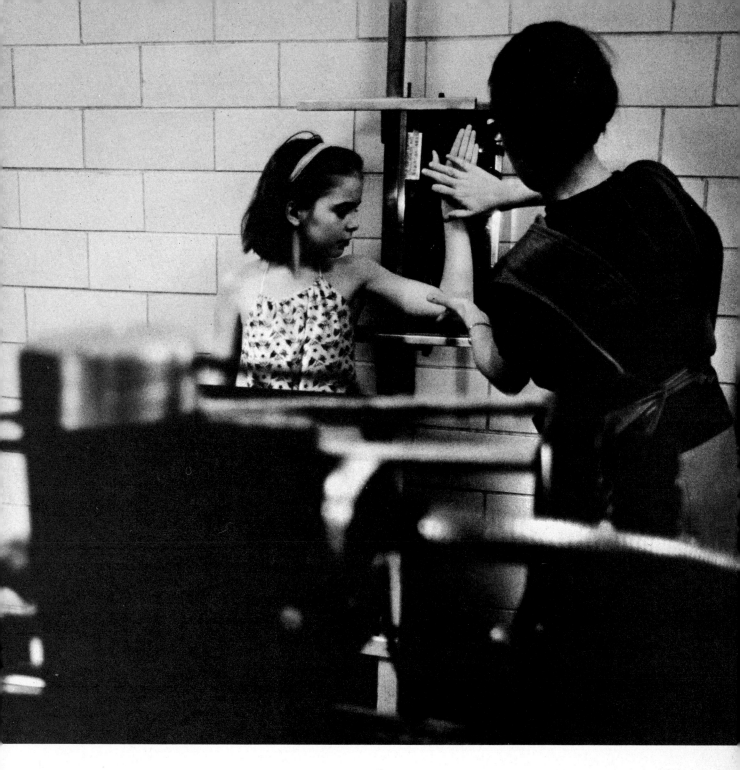

Plotting Curves of Physical Change

Measurements of ordinary physical changes are the routine data basic to any study of growth. From these, averages can be established for particular ages, and the growth patterns of parents and children can be compared. Fels selects its subjects, like Jane Brucker, among the farm, small-town and city people in southwest Ohio, seeking always individuals who are unlikely to move away and so cut short their examinations. The standard measurements include the height standing and height lying (they are seldom exactly the same), chest and calf circumferences. X-ray pictures showing the growth of cartilage into bone are scanned electronically, and their varying shades of gray are compared with the average by computer. Although some 125 X-rays are taken from birth to the 18th year, exposure to radiation is held down by careful shielding and high-speed techniques. By the time a subject is 18, Fels may have some 1,000 pages of data on him.

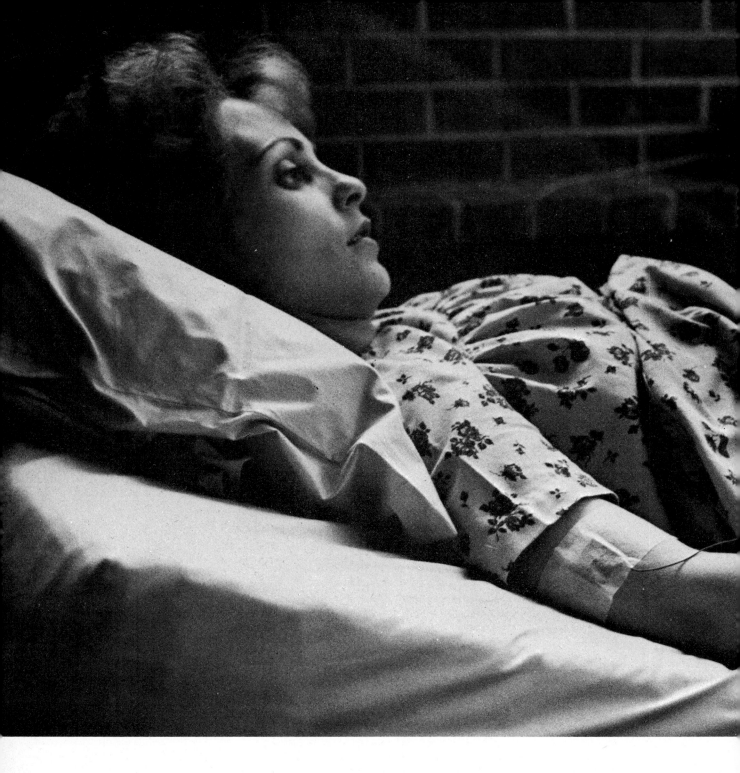

The Behavior of People Unborn

Fels's growth studies begin even before birth. The Institute pioneered in developing methods of examining unborn babies. These include electrocardiograms, from which fetal heartbeats can be classified as slow, fast or unstable, and counts of fetal movements. Babies, it turns out, are more in touch with the outside world before birth than had been thought. If a ringing bell is placed against the mother's abdomen, the baby's heart will beat much faster; if the bell rings often, the baby begins to take the noise more calmly.

Fels studies also confirm the old legend that severe emotional stress in the mother can make the fetus overly active and the newborn child restless and irritable. More recently they have found hints that the fetus' behavior can predict the adult's. An unstable fetal heart rate, for instance, may foreshadow a dependent adult; frequent quick movements may foretell a tendency toward apprehension.

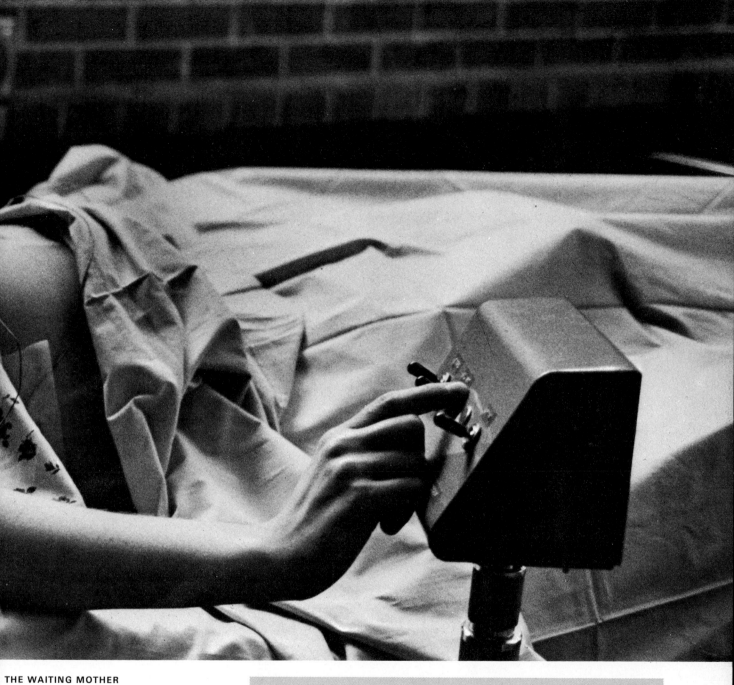

THE WAITING MOTHER
During examination of her minus-two-months-old baby, Mrs. Richard G. Jensen *(above)* rests in a Fels testing room. Electrodes on her arms and stomach pick up both her own and the fetus' heartbeats. She records various movements of the baby by pressing one of the switches.

TWO HEARTS ON ONE RECORD
A section of a polygraph recording *(right)* shows the mother's heartbeats (large circles) and those of her unborn baby (small circles). The heavy bar across part of the bottom of the recording was made when the mother pressed the switch to indicate that the baby was in rapid motion.

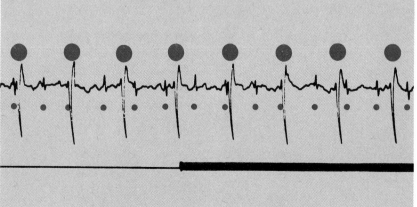

THE FRUSTRATED FEMALE

Separated by a fence from her mother and a tantalizing floorful of toys, Michelle Weber, two, breaks into typically female tears. After it became clear that mother would not help, Michelle tried to climb the fence but soon gave up and stood sobbing until mother finally came *(right)* to calm and console her.

THE ACTIVATED MALE

Confronted by the same barrier, Jaimie Campbell, also two, responds *(left)* in typically aggressive male fashion by trying to swarm over it. Later he sought a way around, then tried to pull it down. Defeated on all fronts, he philosophically began to explore the toyless side of the fence for something else to do.

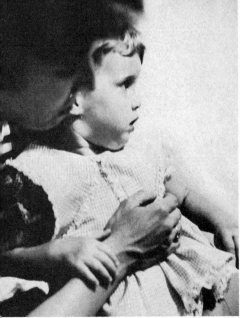

The Reasons Why Boys Will Be Boys

Temperamental differences between the sexes are hardly news. But Fels studies have helped to define these differences and have revealed that some appear as soon as three months after birth. Boys have a shorter attention span than girls. At one year of age, when shown a series of pictures, the boys lose interest more quickly than the girls. Boys are also more independent and aggressive: confronted with a toy in a box, a boy will try to unlatch it while a girl is more likely to turn to mother for help, though she will take no longer to open the box once she tries.

Fels scientists doubt that these differences are innate. Parents, they believe, raise children according to a social pattern that demands independent boys and dependent girls. But these pressures are so subtle as to be almost unnoticeable. For example, the researchers have found that mothers fondle girl babies more often than they do boys, and they are twice as apt to nurse a girl as a boy. In turn, the girl child tends to cling to mother, thus beginning her development into a feminine person.

MARBLES FOR CIRCLES

Psychologist Eugene S. Gollin tells five-year-old Del Staigers to press a lever under the circle *(left)* when both shapes light up. When Del does this, he gets a marble *(foreground)*. Then the solid gray background is changed to gray and white stripes, and Del must press a lever under the triangle. This shift muddles three-year-olds, but children Del's age continue winning marbles.

96

Ups and Downs in Performance

Psychologists formerly believed that children's mental abilities matured in a gradual and orderly manner. This assumption is the basis of the standard I.Q. tests, which compare a child's mental age with his chronological age. But I.Q. tests, it turns out, give far from consistent results. In 1958 Fels published statistics showing that in the period from two and a half to 12 years a child's performance on the tests might soar from a level corresponding to I.Q. 100 (normal) to 140 or more, or drop from 135 to 105. Upward changes of 18 to 70 points occurred in a quarter of the children, downward changes in a fifth. Boys scored large increases twice as often as girls. Fels thinks the tests overlooked variables in boys such as intensified desire and confidence and, in girls, the growing awareness of society's demand that boys be smarter.

BALKED BY HIS YOUTH
Although Del can recognize and copy all of the lines, angles and squares that make up the tilted cross, he cannot draw the cross. The whole eludes him even though he is master of its parts.

However, he is just reaching the age when such skills normally begin to develop very rapidly, and by the time of his next examination he will probably find copying such shapes an easy matter.

THREE GENERATIONS AT FELS
Not only Del but his sisters, parents and maternal grandparents as well *(right)* are being studied by Fels. Scientists at the Institute are seeking to determine in such family examinations whether certain individual traits of physiology are passed on from one generation to the next.

A Boy Responds to Stress

Using closed-circuit TV and a polygraph, a collection of measuring instruments somewhat resembling the so-called lie detector, Fels scientists study physical reactions to psychological stimuli at various ages. They have found, among other things, that simple problems in mental arithmetic can, under certain circumstances, cause massive increases in heart rate and blood pressure. The greatest increases are found in young adults who as schoolchildren were especially interested in high marks. From these and other findings the researchers have concluded that every person has certain "constitutional" traits that influence the way his body's organs respond to stress. These traits may be inherited, acquired in early childhood or both, but they tend to persist throughout life. Thus a boy who "tenses up" over arithmetic problems in school may, as an adult, react the same way to an income-tax blank. The researchers have also found hints of sex differences. In some experiments, for example, the palms of girls' hands perspired more in response to stress than those of boys.

A TENSION WATCHER
Monitoring stress reactions, a technician *(left)* tends a polygraph machine wired to a boy who is being tested in another room, and simultaneously watches him on closed-circuit TV. He takes note of any action the boy makes, for even a yawn or a hiccup can affect the recording.

THE SHAPE OF STRESS

Twelve-year-old Todd Judy's tongue shows the strain as he ponders which of the four abstract shapes before him are most alike *(above)*. A speedup in his breathing rate is measured by the cord around his chest, his more rapid heartbeat by the electrodes attached to his arms.

THE PATTERN OF RESPONSE

Technician William Phillips shows Todd the results of his tests *(below)*. Stress tests are conducted separately from all other Fels examinations and are given at much longer intervals. Because testees are paid for their efforts, the examination is called the "one-buck special."

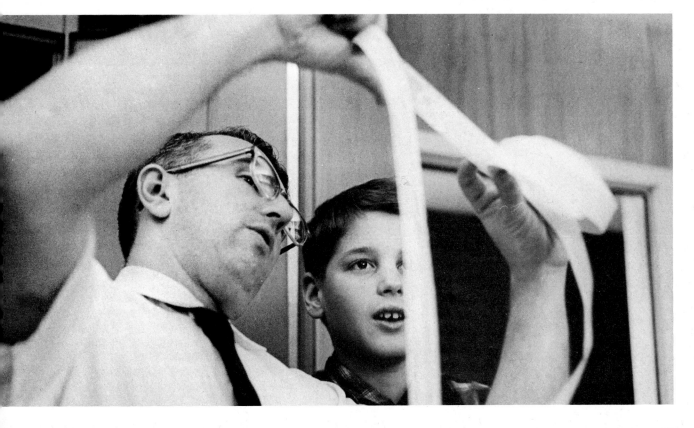

Stand-in for a Little Boy

Certain functions of the developing nervous system can best be studied by inserting delicate instruments into various organs to measure their electrical activity. Since this procedure is impractical in human subjects, Fels uses cats, some of whose reactions closely resemble those of humans. Big Bertha, the cat shown on these pages, has the responses of an overactive, impulsive boy. By studying her nervous system, scientists hope to discover why some boys grow up overactive and impulsive.

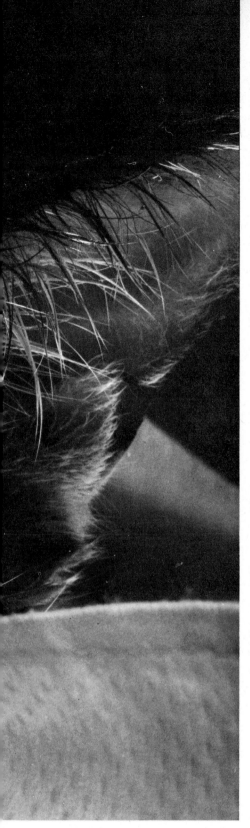

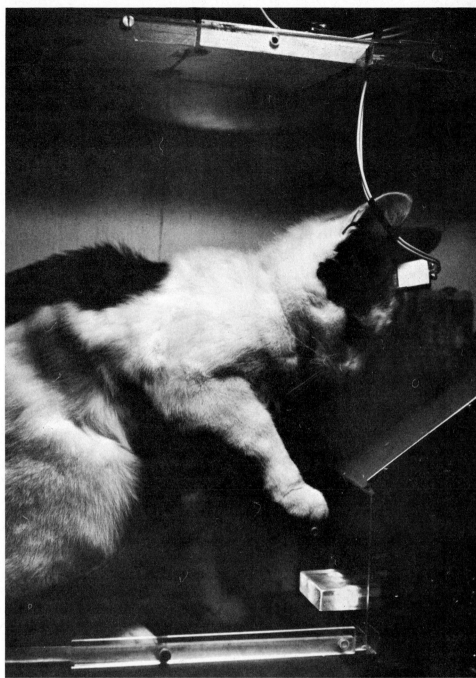

PLUGGED IN AND AT WORK
To earn her food ration, Big Bertha *(above)* presses a lever when it lights up. As she does so, her heartbeats are recorded by an apparatus attached to her head plug through the overhead wires. Like human heartbeats, Big Bertha's slow in pleasant anticipation of food to come.

OPERATION CATNAP
Dead to the world, Big Bertha sleeps off the effects of an anesthetic after an operation to replace a badly functioning electrode near her heart. This electrode picks up the electrical waves generated by heartbeats and transmits them through wires to a plug on the cat's head.

THE LIFE OF AN EDUCATED CAT
Between tests Bertha keeps alert watch on the camera. Cats used in the testing are "recruited" at nearby farms and, despite the experiments of the scientists, they appear to live happy, well-fed lives. They have air-conditioned quarters and are visited regularly by a veterinarian.

Roads into Unknown Realms

Fels studies have moved far beyond the obvious increases in body size that spell growth to most people. Some research projects focus on unexplored aspects of mental and emotional development, such as the intricate interrelationship of the heart and nervous system. One study is attempting to correlate changes in the heartbeat and in brain waves when a light is flashed on the subject's face. As the subject responds, his heart action influences his brain and vice versa. When Fels investigators feel that they have defined this relationship in young adults, they will test younger and older subjects to discover how the relationship develops and how it changes with aging. Meanwhile, they speculate that when the poet sang, "My heart leaps up when I behold a rainbow in the sky," he may have been speaking the scientific truth.

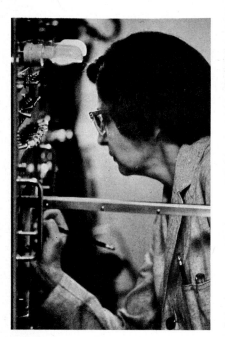

READING THE MIND AND BODY
Psychophysiologist Beatrice Lacey *(above)* takes notes on subject Janet Heinzen's heart response to the light. The array of electrodes attached to Mrs. Heinzen *(right)* record, via the panel behind her, her brain waves, heart rate, blood flow, perspiration and respiration.

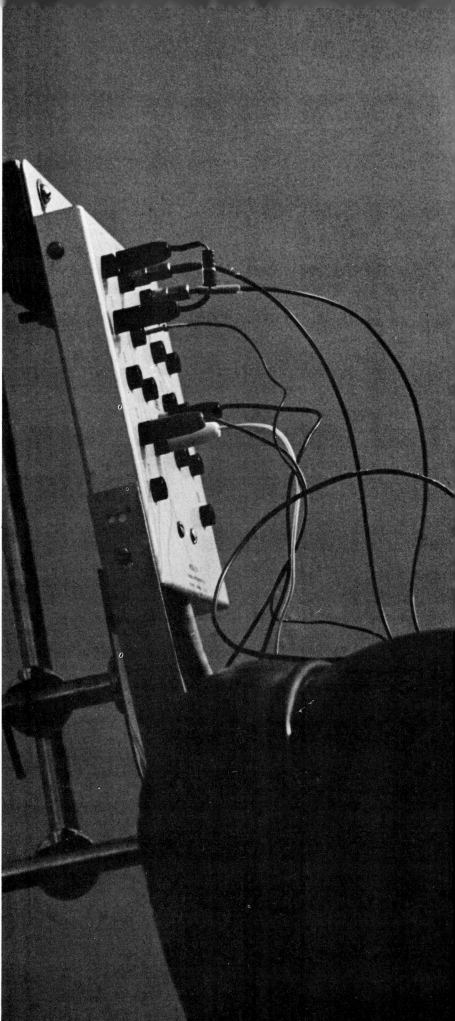

5
The Tempestuous
Years

THE SPURT IN PHYSICAL GROWTH that takes place during adolescence is the most obvious aspect of that transitional period but not the most important. The alterations in appearance that accompany adolescence are merely external evidence of internal processes producing greater changes in the body than it has experienced since birth. The adult is not simply bigger and stronger than the child—he is a different person.

In particular, he is a person who has achieved sexual maturity and fallen heir to all the possibilities and problems this status implies. The physical modifications of adolescence, apart from those which are simply increases in size, are nearly all related in one way or another to this single, central fact. So, too, are many of the psychological changes. Because he is physically a different person, the adolescent must behave differently. But while the physical developments take place automatically, the changes in behavior do not. Most of them must be learned, and the learning process in contemporary Western society is protracted, difficult and often painful for the adolescent—and for his family.

Scientifically, one of the most intriguing puzzles of adolescence is why it happens when it does. We know that it is set off by different hormones secreted by the endocrine system into the bloodstream, and the action of these hormones has already been fairly well traced. But what causes the change? Why should the endocrine glands, which for 10 or 12 years have operated in a fixed, self-regulating pattern, shift to a new one?

The best evidence at present suggests that the whole process begins in the nervous system, in the small mass at the top of the brainstem that is called the hypothalamus. This tiny cluster of nerve cells plays a part out of all proportion to its size in the body's economy. It is the control center for a host of vital functions: it regulates the heartbeat, the rate of breathing, body temperature, and the cycle of wakefulness and sleep. In addition, the hypothalamus appears to act as a kind of biological timer. It turns on the hormonal processes that produce the adolescent growth spurt and sexual maturity; at the proper moment, it turns them off. This it does through its effect on the body's "master" gland, the pituitary, which lies immediately beneath it and which regulates the activity of other endocrine glands.

This description of the hypothalamus' role is based on some experiments conducted on rats. In one, the British physiologist Geoffrey Wingfield Harris and a Swedish colleague, Dora Jacobsohn, removed the pituitary gland from an adult rat and as a substitute grafted on the pituitary of a newborn rat. At once, the new gland started to release the hormones appropriate to an adult. Clearly the infant gland had received a message of some sort from the adult body, which impelled it to this unusual premature activity.

Yet another experiment, also carried out by a binational team, indicated that the message came from the hypothalamus. Dr. B. T. Donovan of London and Dr. J. J. van der Werff ten Bosch of Leiden, Holland, were able to bring laboratory rats to premature puberty simply by damaging a portion of the animals' hypothalamuses. In all other respects, the experimental rats seemed normal: although they were much too small to have reached puberty, they were the proper size for their actual ages.

What the hypothalamus "knows"

These experiments have been interpreted to mean that the hypothalamus regulates the pituitary gland by reacting to some of the body's other hormones. During childhood, it is apparently very sensitive to the small quantity of sex hormones present in the bloodstream even before birth. Responding to their presence, the hypothalamus prevents the pituitary from releasing its gonadotrophic hormones, which would stimulate the sex glands to step up their hormone production.

Science has not yet discovered how the hypothalamus "knows" when the time for puberty has arrived. The process is thought to be connected with the general level of growth and development that the organism has achieved. Whatever the explanation, the hypothalamus at a certain time apparently becomes less sensitive to the sex hormones and ends its inhibition of the pituitary. Then the pituitary is free to release gonadotrophins. These, in turn, prod the sex glands into stepping up their own output and sexual maturation begins. These interlinked processes continue until the sex hormones in the bloodstream reach a level that can stimulate the hypothalamus, which thereupon calls a halt to further sexual changes. Thus the level of sexual development is stabilized.

Since damage to the hypothalamus can bring on premature puberty in rats, it seems likely that tumors or other abnormalities in this tiny region could bring young boys and girls to sexual maturity long before the adolescent growth spurt would normally occur. Examples of this condition have been reported in medical history for centuries. In 1658, a German physician, J. A. von Mandelslo, described the case of a girl who had begun menstruating at the age of three and gave birth to a son when she was six. The most celebrated case in recent times occurred in April of 1939, when a ragged Indian woman from the foothills of the Andes brought her small daughter, Lina, to the hospital at Pisco, Peru. The mother was convinced that her child's bulging belly was a sign of possession by evil spirits. The examining physician, Geraldo Lozado, at first believed that the child was suffering from an abdominal tumor. Both were wrong. Lina was actually eight months pregnant, and in May, Dr. Lozado delivered the 70-pound child of a healthy six-and-a-half-pound boy. Lina's exact age at the time is not clear. According to her birth certificate, made out in the primitive village in which she had been born, she was four years and eight months old. But her developmental age, based on X-rays of her teeth and bones, indicated she was about six.

Fortunately, cases of sexual precocity are rare. In a study made during the 1940s by a British physician, Hugh Jolly, only 69 instances were discovered in the United Kingdom. More than two thirds of these were girls —a disproportion no one has yet been able to explain.

Long-term studies may eventually confirm a strong scientific suspicion aroused by earlier observations of precocious girls: the earlier fertility comes, the longer it lasts. Girls who mature late tend to reach menopause a little earlier than the average woman, who loses her fertility in her late forties. By contrast, the precocious girls described by 18th and 19th Century physicians, who could bear children while still children themselves, did not reach menopause until their fifties.

Premature sexual development seldom brings premature sexual desire. Only one of the girls in Jolly's sample showed any interest in this direction, and only three—16 per cent—of the boys. On the other hand, sexual precocity does seem to affect both mental and physical growth. As children its victims are generally taller than their contemporaries, and therefore usually prefer to play with older girls and boys, who are closer to them in developmental age. Ultimately, however, most of them end up shorter than average, and they are more likely to be mildly retarded mentally than are children who develop according to a normal timetable.

In ordinary children, all the changes associated with puberty occur during the adolescent growth spurt in a relatively coordinated and harmonious fashion. Usually, the outward evidences of emerging maturity begin to show themselves at about the same time that the spurt commences. Boys begin to look like men: their shoulders widen; their hips become proportionately narrower; their legs and arms lengthen and become more muscular. Girls become womanly: their breasts develop, their hips widen, and deposits of fat beneath the skin produce a rounded, feminine contour.

Broad hips, broad shoulders

These alterations in structure, produced by the action of the sex hormones circulating in quantity through the bloodstream, serve obvious functions. Women's broader hips aid in carrying and bearing children. Their fatty deposits provide reserves they can draw on to nourish unborn or infant children when food is in short supply. While women's bodies specialize for child-bearing and feeding, men grow to be providers and protectors. In primitive times, men needed broad shoulders and strong muscles to hunt food and defend their families against predatory enemies, animal or human.

The secondary sex characteristics evolved over millions of years be-

A PUBERTY CEREMONY for girls of an Apache Indian tribe is symbolically depicted in this old painting on doeskin. Each girl being initiated shares a blanket with an old woman "guardian," who is sworn to protect the girl for life. Medicine men in headdresses dance around the fire, which represents cleansing. The stars stand for good will.

cause they were useful. They have survived, it appears, partly because they are still useful in attracting the opposite sex. Though standards of beauty vary enormously from one people to another, a powerful, broad-shouldered man or a curved, feminine-looking woman will evoke interest almost anywhere in the world. In man, as in other species, the secondary sex characteristics appear to act as automatic "releasers" of the mating impulse. Individuals in whom they are well developed are more likely to be chosen as mates, and therefore more likely to pass on the bodily traits that have proven advantageous to the species. (There is some evidence that children as well as grown-ups possess physical releasers. The rounded faces of infants—baby chicks as well as baby boys and girls—may serve to stimulate protective behavior in adults. Because babies are cute, people want to cuddle and nurture them.)

Preparation for biological maturity

The primary sexual changes which prepare the body for reproduction take place at about the same time as the secondary ones. In boys the testes become larger, and inside them the tubules which manufacture sperm come to maturity. The prostate gland develops, and begins to secrete the seminal fluid. The growth and development of these reproductive organs trigger the appearance of two other secondary sex characteristics. These, more than any others, are the ones that announce to the world that the boy has become a man: the deepened voice and the bearded face. In fact, the boy then is in a sense already a man, since these changes usually occur after sexual maturity has been achieved. They are produced by testosterone, the hormone secreted by the testes. As it moves through the bloodstream, it stimulates the growth of facial hair and also stimulates growth in the cartilage of the larynx, thus changing the pitch of the voice.

In girls the growth and development of breasts, uterus and ovaries come first. Shortly after the peak of the growth spurt, the menarche follows. This first announcement of womanhood is sometimes deceptive. Uterus and ovaries do not always develop synchronously, and it sometimes happens that the uterus begins its monthly cycle before the ovaries release mature eggs. Generally, however, no more than a year elapses between the menarche and the attainment of fertility.

All these dramatic physical occurrences are bound to affect the adolescent's feelings about himself and others. The adolescent years are a period of search and questioning. A British physician who specializes in the problems of adolescence, Doris Odlum, lists these as questions the adolescent asks himself:

" 'What sort of person am I?'

'Are my thoughts and feelings similar to those of other people or am I quite different?'

DIFFERENT APPROACHES by the sexes to the same problem are evident even in the preadolescent years. In a series of tests at the University of California, children 11 to 13 years old were given a variety of toys and told to create an "exciting scene." Girls almost always selected and arranged their toys to emphasize inner space, such as the enclosed family scene below. Boys stressed outer space, with elaborate protrusion of rockets and towers. Some psychologists believe the results reflect anatomical as well as mental differences.

'Am I better or worse than other people?'

'Would people want me if they knew what I was really like or would they reject me?'

'What sort of people are my parents?'

'How do they compare with other children's parents?'

'What do I think about my friends?'

'What sort of person do I wish to be?' "

A thousand similar questions are voiced, relating not only to the immediate environment but also to the world in general and the meaning of life itself.

In comparing himself with his contemporaries, the adolescent often focuses on externals. Good looks, however defined, are valued virtually everywhere, so he often measures his worth as a person and his chances of success by the degree to which he meets his society's standards of attractiveness. If he feels inadequate on this score he worries. A physician who examined a group of American adolescents over an eight-year period discovered that a third of the boys and nearly half the girls were concerned about their appearance. Boys fretted because they were short or fat or did not have athletic frames or because they had bad skin—or simply *felt* ugly. Girls worried because they were too tall or fat or generally homely, or because their breasts were small or their figures unformed. Not surprisingly, the late maturers were the most self-critical. They were, after all, at an obvious disadvantage when they compared themselves to others of the same age.

The late maturer

This disadvantage seems to be more acute among boys than among girls. Late-maturing boys' dissatisfactions with themselves are reflected both in the opinions of their classmates and in their own responses to psychological tests. Questionnaires circulated among adolescents reveal that late-maturing boys are more often described as show-offs than those who are early maturers. They are also considered more restless, bossier, less grown-up, less good-looking. And tests of the late maturers indicate that they are more likely to feel rejected, rebellious and aggressive. At the same time they are much more dependent, with a much greater need for psychological support from friends and family. In other words, they tend to be both angry and afraid, a combination that obviously makes for conflict, between the boys and their environment as well as within the boys themselves.

The slow-growing boy's problems are rendered even more acute because his special difficulties are heaped on top of others which affect both boys and girls in the early years of adolescence. Social custom in our society ignores an elementary biological fact: until quite late in the teens, girls outpace boys in development. They reach puberty at a younger age, and they experience psychological changes before their male contemporaries. Surveys of junior high school students show that girls are at least two years ahead of their male classmates in physical development. Many have reached puberty by the time they enter junior high, while many boys have not yet reached puberty when they enter senior high. As a result, during these crucial years boys and girls alike have little opportunity to know members of the opposite sex who are on the same level of development as themselves. At the same time, as anthropologist Margaret Mead points out, many American parents press their preadolescent children to "go steady." As a result, the teenagers are not given enough time to learn the meaning of friendship with members of the same sex. This development Miss Mead finds disturbing. She believes that the capacity to form and keep close friendships with one's own sex can best be developed in childhood and that it is closely related to the ability to achieve mature love relationships in later life.

Are the tensions and anxieties of adolescence dictated by nature or imposed by society? The answer seems to be that they are imposed by society in advanced countries, because society's timetables are not synchronized with man's natural growth timetable.

Of all animals, man is the slowest to reach physical maturity. A cat can have kittens at 12 months, a lioness can produce cubs at about 28 months. Even the great apes, closest to man in their body structure and in intelligence, reach puberty between eight and 12 years. Man's delayed maturity cannot be a biological accident; it must have conferred some evolutionary advantage—i.e., it must be related to his intelligence.

Nearly all human behavior is learned rather than inherited. Man is much less a creature of instinct than any other animal. Indeed, the capacity to learn, to substitute flexible thinking for the rigidities of instinct, is a basic measure of intelligence in man or any other species. But learning is a time-consuming business. Hence man's protracted childhood is a necessity to give him time to acquire the mass of information and skills without which he could not survive as an adult, even on a primitive level.

Society and adolescence

In primitive societies, the years of childhood offer all the learning time an individual needs to fit into his culture. As a result, sexual maturity and social maturity are reached almost simultaneously. The in-between period is at most two or three years.

In modern industrialized societies, the situation is very different. These complex cultures demand complex skills and complex behavior habits which cannot possibly be acquired in a baker's dozen of years. The

HUMAN LIFE EXPECTANCY is more than three times that of any other mammal shown in the graph below, in which the darker shade represents childhood. This graph is based on longevity and puberty records of animals in captivity and human beings in countries which enjoy a high standard of living. No explanation has been found for man's long life-span, apart from the self-evident fact that his body is more durable.

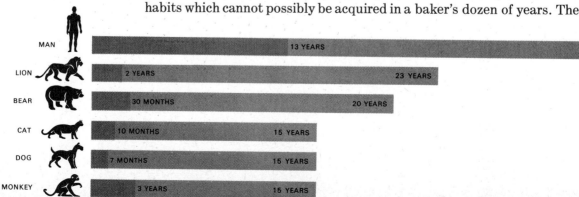

MAN	13 YEARS	
LION	2 YEARS	23 YEARS
BEAR	30 MONTHS	20 YEARS
CAT	10 MONTHS	15 YEARS
DOG	7 MONTHS	15 YEARS
MONKEY	3 YEARS	15 YEARS

time lapse between sexual and social maturity is therefore long and drawn-out. In most Western countries, few people achieve economic independence before the late teens, and those who go on to higher education must wait until their twenties. The intervening years are a no-man's-land. The adolescent is no longer physically dependent, as he was in childhood, but he is still a dependent psychologically and economically. He is increasingly held responsible for his actions, yet still controlled and supported by his parents. Generally he is physically ready for an adult sex relationship long before he is considered ready, economically or psychologically, for marriage.

"The lesson of not caring"

The contrast between adolescence in primitive and in modern societies is pointed up in studies of two primitive cultures. These studies, which are classics in the field, were conducted by Margaret Mead at the very beginning of her long and distinguished career as an anthropologist. During the 1920s she spent six months among the people of Tau, a tiny island in the Samoan group, and a similar period among the Manus, an equally primitive people of New Guinea. The two cultures differ from each other in almost every respect save one: in neither is adolescence a time of stress and conflict. In both places, boys become men and girls become women without any of the anxieties and emotional difficulties that are considered inevitable in the U.S.

The Samoans are a people who have made the casual, nonchalant and debonair approach to the world a way of life. "No one plays for very high stakes, no one pays very heavy prices, no one suffers for his convictions or fights to the death for special ends," Miss Mead writes in her book *Coming of Age in Samoa*. "No implacable gods, swift to anger and strong to punish, disturb the even tenor of their days. . . . No one is hurried along in life or punished harshly for slowness of development." Everyone does his job, and strives to do it well. Words like "intensity," "ambition" and "competition" have virtually no meaning at all to the people of Tau. Samoa, says Miss Mead, "is kind to those who have learned the lesson of not caring, and hard upon those individuals who have failed to learn it."

In this bland, perhaps shallow, culture, all the events of life, from birth through death, are simply taken in stride. The child is not shielded from any of them as he grows. Sex and procreation, growth and development, are all accepted without fuss, and the Samoan youngster slides from childhood into puberty almost imperceptibly. No one is concerned about a girl's first menstruation, and she herself takes it completely for granted. Nor does it alter her social position in any way. By the time she reaches the menarche she has already graduated from her childhood task of taking care of her younger brothers and sisters. She still has some years before she will take on woman's work: weaving, bark-stripping, fishing, light farming.

A couple of years after she arrives at puberty, the Samoan girl is admitted to the group of older girls and becomes her culture's version of a debutante. She spends her days primarily in sleeping and her nights in dancing and making love. In time, she chooses from among her many lovers the young man whom she likes best, marries him and settles down. For a Samoan girl, adolescence is the happiest period of her life.

"No word for love"

The Manus is a radically different person from the Samoan. "The whole of life, his most intimate relation to people, his conception of places, his evaluation for his guarding spirits, all fall under the head of *kawas,* 'exchange,'" says Miss Mead in *Growing Up in New Guinea.* "He has no other word for friend. . . . Friends are people with whom one trades, or who help one in trade. . . . Pregnancy, birth, betrothal, marriage, death, are thought of in terms of . . . shell money, pigs and oil."

Manus men and women, antagonistic and hostile to one another, view every natural function of the body with shame and disgust. "The Manus language has no word for love, no word for affection or caress." Parents arrange marriages when their offspring are still children. A girl whose father has not been able to buy her a husband by the time she reaches puberty becomes an object of pity in the community. When she achieves menarche, the Manus girl's family marks the fact with an elaborate public ceremony, which touches off a whole round of party-giving and exchanges of property and food between her family and the family of her betrothed. But the girl herself plays little part in all these festivities. For five days and nights she sits in a special room, without washing and hardly moving, guarded at night by other village girls. Thereafter come more feasts, more ceremonies, canoe parades, exchanges of beadwork and food, and a series of vainglorious and pretentious speeches—by the chiefs, by the girl's father and by the father of her betrothed.

Several years elapse between these bleak celebrations and the girl's marriage. During this period, her standing in the community is in no wise changed; her work and her relationships with others remain the same. The only difference is that she has reached puberty—and must keep all evidence of this shameful event concealed. "Forbidden to go abroad in the dark night, she lies awake and listens to the hour-long colloquies between mortals and spirits," writes Miss Mead. "Except for the unusual intrusion of a brief and penalty-ridden sex affair, these years are not years of storm and stress, nor are they years of placid unfolding of the personality. . . . In Manus, a girl has no need to seek a husband; he has been found. She may not seek a lover; she is denied the outlet of close friendship with other girls. She simply waits, growing taller and more womanly in figure, and in spite of herself, wiser in the ways of her world."

By Western standards, the Manus way of life is stultifying in the extreme. The concepts of freedom and choice are as foreign to it as are the words for love or friend. But if Manus life is grim, it is at least secure. There, as among the more permissive Samoans, the adolescent knows at every moment what the future holds in store. The pattern of his life is fixed by tradition and he is spared the pain and conflict of having to make choices or decisions independently.

The adolescent in Western societies, coping with the lengthening gap between physical and social maturity, must at the same time discover who he is, what he wants, what he believes to be "good" and "bad." Among the Samoans or Manus he would not need to ask such questions. The values of such societies, whether pleasant or unpleasant by our standards, are simple and consistent, and he absorbs them without thinking. By contrast, Western cultures—particularly American society —present the adolescent with a bewildering variety of options: in religious affiliation, political belief, vocational possibilities, hobbies and leisure-time pursuits. The search for values and goals, difficult even for an adult, is doubly difficult for the adolescent. Often he cannot decide which way to turn. Shall he go back to the protected world of childhood dependence and submission to authority? Or should he take a chance and move forward to independence and adult responsibility?

Rebellion and protection

Because the answers he puzzles out for himself are often confused and equivocal, his behavior is likely to swing from one extreme to another. Often he rebels most vociferously against orders from the adult world when what he really wants is to be protected by it. Often, too, his parents and his culture are not much help. They prod him to grow up and to be independent, but cannot give him the economic means of achieving this goal. They may encourage him to "go steady" at an early age, but they caution him against sex. They permit him to drive a car when he is 16, and consider him old enough to fight for his country only two years later. But not until he is 21 does his vote give him a voice in determining how his society shall be governed.

Because the adult world itself is so frequently unsure of just what it wants from youth, it may hesitate to assume the authority that is in fact its prerogative. From World War I until the middle 1950s, American parents became increasingly permissive in dealing with their children. Lacking guidance from those who were older and more experienced, the children turned to each other, creating a subculture with its own distinctive clothing and behavior, its own heroes and villains, its own language, music and beliefs. Instead of coming increasingly to feel a part of the broader society, adolescents became increasingly alienated from it.

This trend had begun to reverse itself by the time the 1960s arrived. Overpermissiveness in child-rearing was then beginning to go out of fashion. The very flamboyance—and sometimes violence—of the adolescent subculture awakened psychologists and sociologists to the gravity of the problem.

Solutions to this problem will always be slow and partial. As more and more young people go in for postgraduate study, the time gap that higher education imposes between physical and social maturity is likely to become longer, not shorter. As the college population swells, the gap will affect more, not fewer, young people. The many decisions which the adolescent must make to define his identity will not decrease in number, though they may become easier. But a return to the simpler and more static world of the past, let alone the world of Samoa or New Guinea, is of course impossible. Though awareness of the adolescent's problems may point the way to alleviating them, a measure of tension, anxiety and even pain while growing up seems to be part of the price exacted for civilization and freedom.

Ordered Designs and Patterns

The growth of every creature on earth is precisely regulated in accordance with exact patterns. These patterns dictate that every human being, for example, shall have fingerprints, and that all flamingos shall have long legs. So precise are these patterns that the offspring they produce are often exquisite examples of form and symmetry. This regulation governs not only size and shape, but also the timetable by which a given animal will develop. Even so, adequate allowance is made for individuality. No two human fingerprints are ever exactly the same; no two chickens have identical sets of feathers, and no two oysters ever have identical shells. Within each species further individuality comes about as a result of each individual adaptation to environment. The muscles of a man who does heavy work will increase in size more than those of a sedentary man, no matter what the muscular man's original growth pattern may have called for.

REGULATED BUT RANDOM
The ridges on a human thumb *(opposite)* help fit the human hand for its basic function: grasping objects. The pattern of ridges is determined by the growth of papillae, minute elevations beneath the skin that contain capillaries and sometimes nerve endings. A random element in the growth of these papillae produces a pattern that is never exactly the same from one individual to another.

STRIPES FOR CAMOUFLAGE
The showy black and white stripes of the zebra's coat would seem to make it highly visible. But in fact they blend with the zebra's environment and help it to elude the eyes of predators.

AN AERODYNAMIC DESIGN
The tip of a crane feather *(left)* reveals the loose structure common to bird plumes. Their design reduces friction and air turbulence during flight and provides warmth at other times.

Form to Fit Function

The patterns of growth by which individual animals have adjusted to their environment have produced designs that are often striking. Just how these different patterns came into being is obscured in the antiquity of evolution. However they came about, patterns such as those shown here serve specific functions. A bird's feathers are designed to prevent air friction; the zebra's hide offers protective camouflage; the teeth of a skate are steadily replaced by new ones to keep up with its growth; coral skeletons build on one another for strength.

But nowhere is this adaptation for specialized function more evident than in the insect world, whose numbers are estimated to exceed five million species. For example, the water-dwelling whirligig beetle has one pair of eyes for seeing things in the air and a second set for underwater viewing. The tiger beetle is equipped with a pair of barbed spurs on its back, with which it anchors itself against the wall of its underground burrow in case its prey is big enough to pull it out of the ground. All such structural characteristics are the result of growth patterns that determine the final appearance of living organisms.

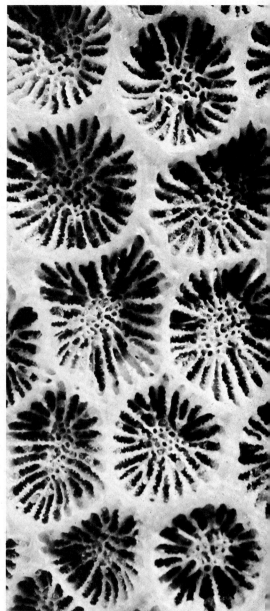

HOMES OF CORAL POLYPS
Looking like a cluster of fluted cupcake holders, the skeletal remains of individual coral polyps are nested together. For protection against the surf, each polyp encircles itself in a skeleton.

AN ARSENAL OF TEETH
Rows of replacement teeth bristle from the jaw of a skate. The skate continually sheds its old teeth as it grows, replacing the ones it loses with the next older ones growing in the row behind.

117

Polarity in Growth

In nearly all organisms, from the single-celled paramecium to the most complex mammal, the first and most important expression of the growth pattern is polarity—the basic indication of the direction in which a creature develops. In most organisms, this direction is established in the egg and becomes apparent the first time the egg divides. This cleavage establishes a line—generally a longitudinal, or head-to-tail, axis around which the entire creature is organized. Some organisms, such as the starfish, may exhibit radial symmetry, a pattern suited to their needs. In higher animals, the head-to-tail axis forms a line around which the creature's symmetrical structures develop, though all of these creatures include asymmetrical structures as well. Some very simple animals, such as the amoeba and certain sponges, exhibit an asymmetrical structure.

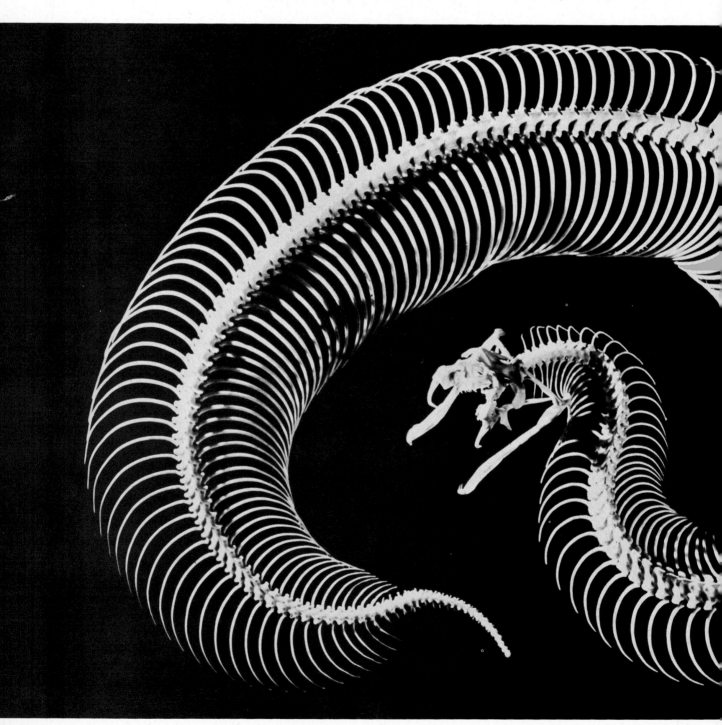

A SYMMETRICAL SERPENT

This skeleton of a four-foot-long Gaboon viper *(below)* is one of the most elaborate examples of bilateral symmetry along the head-to-tail, or longitudinal, axis. Its 160 paired, movable ribs extend from the creature's central spinal column to form an exactly balanced pattern.

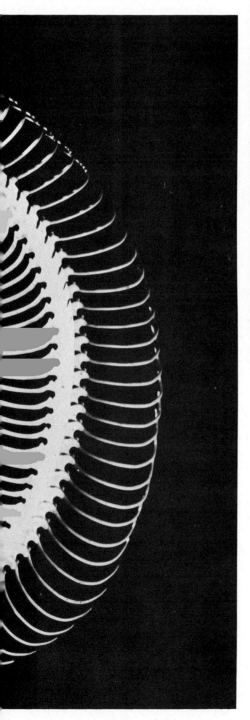

RAYS FROM A CENTER

Radial symmetry is best represented in the external structure of the starfish *(above)*. Being a relatively inactive creature, the starfish must gather its food from its immediate environment. Sense organs in the arms enable the starfish to search out nourishment in every direction.

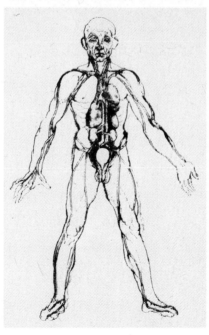

ASYMMETRY WITHIN SYMMETRY

Man's external form is bilateral: the left side is an almost perfect mirror image of the right. Internally, however, there is much asymmetry, as this Da Vinci sketch *(left)* shows. Heart and stomach, for example, are on the left, liver on the right. The intestines lie in asymmetrical coils.

119

Lifeless Forms on Living Bodies

A man's fingernails, a ram's horns and a snail's shell share an important characteristic: all are produced by a type of growth called accretion. In human beings accretionary growth is predominantly displayed in toenails, hair and bone. In these structures, living cells cast off nonliving matter which accumulates outside the cells. The fingernail, for instance, grows from the epidermis, which secretes a soft, lifeless substance called keratin. This matter forces previously secreted keratin out from under the cuticle and forward, where it hardens and dries into a solid plate. Accretionary growth often produces the spiral shapes that many organisms exhibit in their horns or shells. These spirals are created because more matter is produced on one side than the other, since there is an uneven secretion at the growth base. If, for example, the secretionary rate is greater at the front of a horn than at the back, a rearward spiral will develop. This pattern, typical of horned animals such as sheep and goats, is also found in the shells of many mollusks.

A ROLLED-UP CONE

Spiral accretion is perhaps most perfectly represented by the nautilus shell *(right)*. The accretion rate on the animal's upper and outer edges exceeds that on its inner surface. In addition, as the nautilus grows, its secreting base enlarges and fashions bigger and bigger whorls.

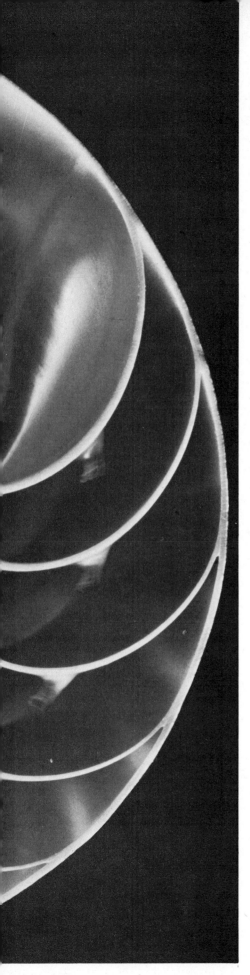

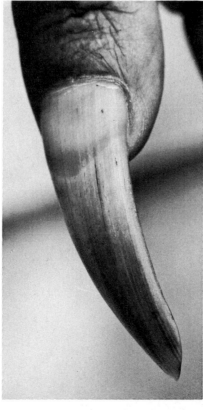

BIDIRECTIONAL GROWTH

A ram's horn *(above)* spirals in two planes. Its base is triangular, and no two of the three sides secrete at the same rate. Thus the pushing force is outward as well as backward. The corrugated pattern reflects periodic growth, each ring representing a specific period of growth.

ACCRETION IN MAN

A professional trademark, this long, tapering thumbnail *(left)* identifies its Taiwanese bearer as a fortune-teller. When human fingernails or toenails are permitted to grow long, they form accretionary spirals of the same type that characterize the ram's horn and the nautilus shell.

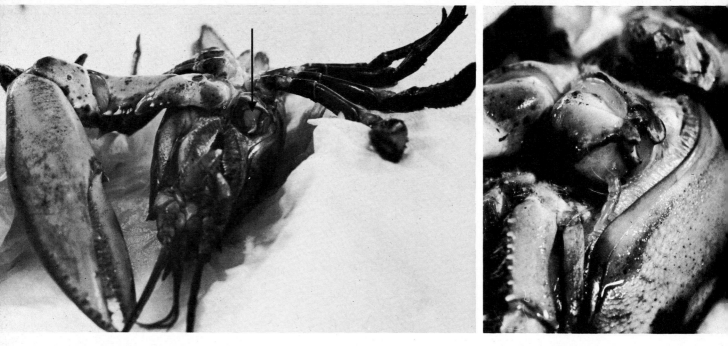

THE REGENERATION CYCLE

This series of pictures shows the progressive stages in the regeneration of a lobster's claw —a process that takes about three years. The animal above lost its left claw near the base (arrow) a few weeks earlier. The wound has now healed and a half-inch-long appendage has grown out—the delicate bud of a new claw that will eventually replace the missing limb.

EARLY MONTHS OF GROWTH

Membranous, translucent tissue that will ultimately be a functioning claw grows downward, as seen in the center of this close-up. The bud, about an inch long, still has no shell covering it.

HEALED BUT NOT WHOLE

In regeneration, man is far less capable than the lobster, as shown in this 17th Century print of two badly crippled veterans. Pointing out that the soldiers are permanently crippled, the sign above observes sardonically that the two men are now less useful than one whole man.

A Renewal Pattern

All organisms to some extent have the ability to replace destroyed, defective or damaged tissue with new growths. This capacity, a pattern of growth called regeneration, varies widely from species to species, and in man and other complex animals it is severely limited. The human potential for regeneration does not go much beyond the healing of wounds, the production of new blood cells, the replacement of tissue in broken bones and in some internal organs. In contrast, such lowly animals as lobsters, crabs and salamanders can replace entire limbs, and flatworms or hydras can grow entire new bodies from a small fragment.

Man's inability to match the regenerative power of many organisms far beneath him on the evolutionary scale has long been a biological puzzle. One often-expressed theory postulates that man's own complexity poses such great problems that an orderly regrowth of the many sorts of tissues involved becomes impossible. This concept, however, does not explain the remarkable regenerative power of the newt. Its limbs are very nearly as complicated as man's, but it can regenerate all four legs if necessary.

In those animals capable of regeneration, the new growth appears to originate as nonspecialized cells. Like the cells of the young embryo, they can develop into any of several types of tissue. These curious cells may be a nonspecialized kind which the adult retains, or they may be cells which, for unknown reasons, revert back to the embryonic state. It is also believed that the hormones and nerve fibers play a determining role in the regenerative process.

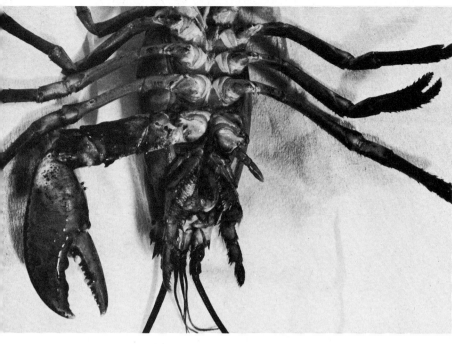

SIZE BUT NOT STRENGTH

At eight months, the regenerating claw is now about two inches long. It has begun growing its protective shell and in a few months will split along the white stripe running down the center to form its characteristic pincers. The greatest amount of the limb's structure is established during the first year. During the last two years of growth it merely gets bigger and stronger.

THE YEAR-OLD CLAW

Within a few days the pincers of this already well-defined claw will separate and it will become fully functional. Lobsters, like crabs, are also capable of regenerating smaller limbs.

Fully regenerated, the claw is smaller than the last one, and always will be. Each time a limb is lost, regenerating power diminishes.

Hypertrophy: Response to Strain

When illness, surgery or exercise places prolonged, abnormal strains upon certain portions of the body, the tissues affected respond by toughening or increasing in size—a pattern known as hypertrophy, or compensatory growth. When a man's kidney is removed, for instance, the other kidney will grow much larger, enabling it to handle a double work load. Similarly, hard physical labor requires that an extra supply of oxygen be conveyed to the muscles, a need that the heart meets by enlarging to increase its blood-pumping capacity. The most obvious example of hypertrophy in man is in the area of muscle development. The powerful arms and chest of the oarsman and the bulging legs of the dancer are testimony to years of intense physical activity. Little is known of the mechanics of compensatory growth, but it differs from other growth patterns in two important ways: during the period of development, new cells are not added; instead, existing cells enlarge. Compensatory hypertrophy does not involve the genes and therefore cannot be passed on to the next generation.

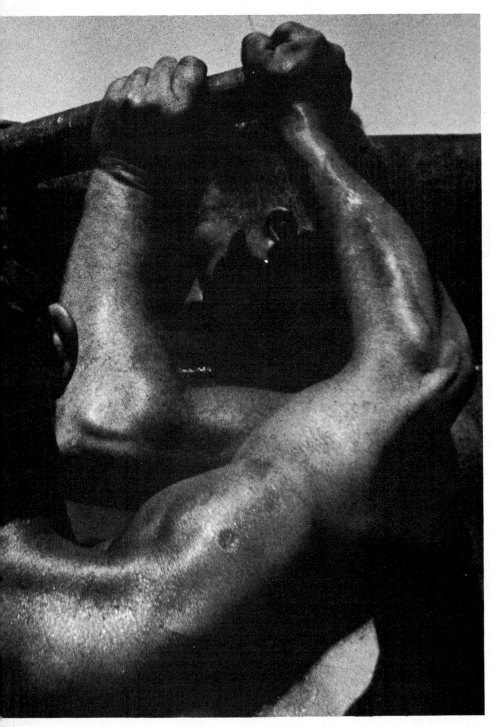

ON THE MARK
Olympic contenders *(opposite)* spring forward at the start of a track race. Their muscles, shaped for speed and strength by years of training, would revert to normal or even become flabby—a condition of atrophy—if these athletes were to adopt a sedentary way of life.

SOMETIMES GOOD, SOMETIMES NOT
Habitual hard labor has produced the bulging muscles of these workers straining to lift a heavy load. Hypertrophy is a useful condition in this case, or in an athlete's heart that has grown bigger and stronger to meet the extra physical needs. But in the case of a heart enlarged by disease, as often happens with high blood pressure, hypertrophy is very undesirable.

Proportional Patterns

The head of a newborn baby, like the legs of a newly foaled colt, seems out of proportion with the rest of its body. However, as in all creatures, the proportions of the baby and the colt will change from infant to adult. The baby's head and the colt's legs grow much more slowly than their other parts. These changes in proportion show that the various parts of the body have different rates of growth. Growth rates also differ from one species to another.

It has been postulated that alterations in growth rates have played a part in the evolutionary process. This concept originated with a British biologist, the late Sir D'Arcy Wentworth Thompson, who compared the physical characteristics of many related species. Through these comparisons, Thompson showed, for example, that two related kinds of fishes could have evolved structural differences merely through shifts in the relative growth rates of different parts—a faster-growing fin in one, a faster-growing head in the other (below).

These variations, clearly visible in related species, are also quite obvious within the same species. Even a cursory examination of any group of human faces will reveal the enormous diversity resulting from slight differences in the growth rates of people's eyes, noses and mouths.

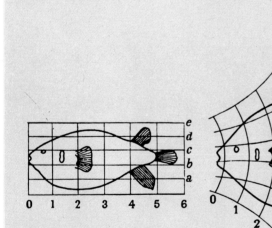

A CHANGED FISH
The concept of different growth rates was shown by these drawings in Sir D'Arcy W. Thompson's book, *On Growth and Form*. Taking one species of fish, he systematically altered its proportions and came up with a fish of markedly different appearance. In effect, he was altering the growth rates of various parts of the fish's anatomy.

A LEGGY COLT
The foal standing by its mother *(right)* is an example of differential growth rates. The foal's body must do much more growing than the legs to attain the proportions of its mother.

Structured Relationships

If an ant were as big as a horse, could it move mountains? No. A giant ant would be a structural failure. Its legs would cave in under it. The weight of a supersized ant would increase as the cube of its height, but the strength of its legs, which depends on their cross-sectional area, would only increase as the square of the height. Thus an ant of only 10 times average size would be 1,000 times heavier—but its legs would only be 100 times stronger.

In growth, the proportions of any organism must be shaped to suit its individual and environmental needs.

EXTREMES IN STRUCTURE

Five flamingos *(above),* each weighing about seven pounds, are supported on pipestem legs half an inch wide. The elephant at right, which weighs 14,000 pounds, needs four thick col- umns, each 14 inches in diameter, to provide it with sufficient underpinning. Were flamingos to grow to an elephant's weight, their legs would be only six inches wide—and would collapse.

6
Genes, Hormones and Environment

IN THE PROCESS OF GROWTH, the genes, hormones and environment work neither in isolation nor in sequence. Instead, they work upon one another, backward as well as forward, to control the order and timing of development. Genes and environment interact from the moment life begins. In the embryo, growth and development are the products of an interplay between the inherited material of the genes and the cellular environment around them. The interaction between genes and hormones is equally intricate and still only partially understood. The most common view has been that the genes alone determine all the structures and functions associated with such characteristics as sex. In this view, genes cause hormones to be secreted. The hormones then act upon various tissues, thus serving as intermediaries in carrying out the genes' instructions.

Investigations suggest that this interpretation is too simple, for hormones can also act directly upon genes. In one experiment, the bodies of roosters were made to behave like those of hens. Hens' livers, stimulated by the action of the female sex hormone estrogen, normally produce a protein that shows up in egg yolk. The livers of roosters do not. Yet when roosters are injected with estrogen, their livers begin to make this substance. The hormone apparently does this by activating a gene in the liver cells which would not otherwise have been called into play.

Despite the constant interaction of the three determinants, some growth factors can be examined independently of others. Some traits are known to be genetically determined, and to be very little influenced either by the environment or by the action of the hormones. Blood type and eye color are examples. These are passed on from parent to child in accordance with the simple laws described in 1866 by the Austrian monk Gregor Johann Mendel, whose plant-breeding experiments first established the science of genetics. Characteristics like these are known to be influenced by a relatively small number of genes. But other traits involve large numbers of genes; in addition, most are known to be strongly influenced by environment as well as inheritance. For these reasons, they are more difficult to study. Fortunately, however, identical twins provide a way of examining them. Because they arise from the splitting of a single fertilized egg, identical twins are born with identical genes. If the geneticist can prove that identical twins share a specific characteristic more frequently than do fraternal twins or ordinary brothers and sisters, he can conclude that the trait is at least partly genetic in its origin.

Height, build and intelligence appear to be among these traits. So is the rate of growth. On the average, identical twins reach menarche within two months of each other, while fraternal twins often attain this landmark a year apart. A study conducted in 1940 among Los Angeles City College coeds confirms the conclusion that age of menarche is influenced by genetic factors. All the girls in the sample attended the same

PITUITARY EXPERIMENT
The dwarfed rat opposite weighs less than a quarter as much as its companion, a normal animal of the same age. Its stunted growth was caused by removal of its pituitary, the "master" endocrine gland. Attached to the underside of the brain, the pituitary secretes at least six hormones. One stimulates growth directly, others through endocrine glands elsewhere in the body.

school and all lived in similar environments. But their genetic backgrounds were not the same and the age of menarche varied in accordance with this difference. Girls of Mexican origin began menstruating at an average age of 12.5 years; girls of Chinese parentage at 13.9 years; and girls of European, Japanese and Negro backgrounds at ages between these extremes.

In addition to the age at which puberty is attained, the general pattern of a child's growth also seems to be controlled primarily by genetic factors. Ordinarily, the growth curves of siblings bear only a general resemblance to one another. But this is not true of identical twins, whose growth curves are almost always similar and often nearly exactly the same. The bodies of the twins, in other words, appear to be responding virtually identically to the messages of their identical genes.

Hormones: chemical messengers of growth

Why do specific genes become active at specific times? The answer does not seem to lie in the genes alone, for the hormones also play a part.

The first of these substances to be recognized was secretin, discovered in 1902 by William Bayliss and Ernest Starling. Produced in the small intestine, secretin travels through the bloodstream to the pancreas, where it stimulates the secretion of the pancreatic juices. Soon after they found the chemical, Bayliss and Starling realized that it was only one of a class of substances, each produced in a specific organ, each traveling to another organ to do its work. Later they named them hormones (from the Greek *hormon*, "to stir up").

Since that time dozens of hormones have been discovered. Most of them are produced by the endocrine, or ductless, glands, which discharge their secretions directly into the bloodstream or into body fluids. Because hormones regulate metabolic processes and since growth depends upon metabolism, all hormones contribute to growth, at least to some extent. But certain hormones have the specific function of promoting growth, or they trigger the great turning points in human development. Any study of human growth must therefore focus upon these hormones and upon the glands which produce them: the pituitary, the thyroid, the adrenals and the gonads, or sex glands.

The ultimate control over the activities of all the growth glands rests with a portion of the brain, the hypothalamus. Second in command is the pituitary gland. Not only does the pituitary produce a hormone directly responsible for growth, it also secretes trophic (nourishing) hormones which speed up the activity of the other growth glands.

Our information on the pituitary has its beginning point with the hobby of a London surgeon of the 18th Century, John Hunter. Hunter's dominating interest was to assemble a systematic medical collection, the largest of its kind. As part of his collection, he wanted the body of a famous giant of the day—an Irishman called Charles Byrne, who claimed to be eight foot four inches tall. (He was, in fact, a mere seven foot seven, as his skeleton, still on view in London, shows.) Learning that Hunter wanted his cadaver, the giant asked his friends to encase it in lead after his death and sink it at sea. The story goes that Hunter bribed the undertakers as they were just about to sink the body, bought it for £500, and added it to his collection.

In 1909—126 years after Byrne's death—the great American neurosurgeon Harvey Cushing, who had recently embarked on a study of the pituitary, examined the giant's skull. He discovered that Byrne had been the victim of a pituitary tumor: deformation of bone in the area of the gland indicated that it had been considerably enlarged.

Earlier, at the end of the 19th Century, the French physiologist Pierre Marie had demonstrated a connection between pituitary tumors and acromegaly, the disease in which parts of the head, hands and feet begin growing again long after normal growth has stopped. Since that time, medicine had suspected that the pituitary played a part in growth disorders. Cushing's study confirmed these suspicions, but it still did not establish precisely how the pituitary influenced growth.

Rats, research and the pituitary

In the '20s Herbert M. Evans of the University of California, one of the greatest modern endocrinologists, shifted the focus of research from the pituitary itself to the hormones it produces. Working with Joseph Long, Evans prepared an extract from the pituitaries of cattle and injected it into the body cavities of baby rats. His rats became giants, double the size and weight of normal adults. But despite their size they were not true adults. Sexually, they remained immature. In the 1930s came a major breakthrough when Evans isolated the substance in his extract which was directly responsible for growth, and labeled it growth hormone. Not until 1944 was it possible to prepare growth hormone in a pure form. By that time, scientists had come to realize that the pituitary is a far more complex organ than anyone had imagined.

Not all the many hormones the pituitary secretes are directly involved in growth, nor do all four of the hormones that influence growth operate directly. Although the hormone Evans isolated does work directly to stimulate growth, the other three act indirectly by stimulating other glands. Thyrotrophic hormone speeds up the activity of the thyroid gland; adrenocorticotrophic hormone, or ACTH, affects the outer layers of the adrenals; and gonadotrophic hormone stimulates the gonads (the ovaries and testes).

The thyroid gland is a butterfly-shaped mass of tissue near the base

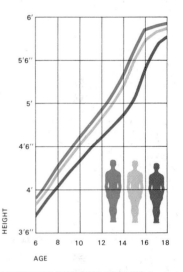

TRIPLETS' GROWTH CURVES from six to 18 demonstrate the genetic control of growth. Two members of the triplet set are genetically identical *(light and dark brown)* and their genes have resulted in very similar curves. The third triplet is nonidentical, or fraternal *(black)*. Since the triplets shared a similar environment, the dissimilar curve of the fraternal member must have resulted mainly from his different complement of genes.

of the neck. It secretes at least two major hormones, very similar in structure and effects to one another. The one that is produced in the largest quantity is thyroxine. Essentially, thyroxine stimulates metabolism and the differentiation and development of the bones, working with the pituitary growth hormone to produce a mature skeletal structure. The thyroid needs iodine to function properly. If iodine is not provided in sufficient quantity in the diet, the gland becomes enlarged and a goiter develops. The discovery in 1905 of the relationship between the thyroid gland and dietary iodine led, after nearly 20 years of experimentation, to the practice of adding iodine to salt.

The hormones produced by the adrenal glands and the gonads work in a totally different way: rather than acting to promote a steady increase in height and weight, they bring about abrupt changes in the overall pattern of growth.

At puberty, when the final stage of growth begins, the adrenals and gonads become active with dramatic suddenness. The pituitary begins to secrete large quantities of gonadotrophins. Under their influence, the testes and ovaries produce the hormones that bring the secondary sex characteristics to maturity. The boy becomes a man; the girl, a woman. At the same time, the adrenals begin to work as growth glands.

The adrenal: stimulus of the growth spurt

In the male, adrenal hormones called androgens collaborate with testosterone, an androgen produced in the testes, to stimulate the enormous spurt in growth that marks adolescence. Adrenal androgens also appear to cause the somewhat smaller growth spurt that girls experience.

The adrenals do not seem to increase their production of androgens because of stimulation from the pituitary, for there is no evidence that more ACTH is produced in adolescence than in childhood. Some endocrinologists believe that the adrenals simply become more sensitive to ACTH at adolescence, and point to animal experiments which show that the ovarian hormones seem to sensitize the adrenals in this way. The theory—it is no more than that—is not wholly convincing, for it does not explain why male adrenals should be sensitized too.

The testes begin producing hormones as early as the fetal stage of growth, when they stimulate the formation of male genitalia in the embryo. At Oxford University, Geoffrey Wingfield Harris has been conducting experiments with rats which indicate that these hormones also affect the hypothalamus. A male rat cannot normally maintain the functioning of the ovary; if an ovary is transplanted from a female to a male, it will stop releasing eggs. Harris was able to alter this pattern. He castrated male rats within three days of their birth and later, when they had become adults, transplanted ovaries into them. Under these circumstances, the ovaries continued to function normally. From one point of view, Harris had simply created interesting—and somewhat horrifying—sexual freaks. From another, he had uncovered a hitherto unsuspected relationship between the hypothalamus and the male sex hormones.

It is the hypothalamus that maintains normal ovarian function in a female rat. By castrating his male rat subjects, Harris removed their source of sex hormones. He drew this conclusion from his experiments: at some point within the first three days after birth, the hypothalamus of a male rat receives a message from the testes "telling" it that it is male, and the message is carried by the hormones. If the hypothalamus does not receive this message it will remain female in type. Normally, an organism's genetic makeup dictates that the sex of the hypothalamus and the rest of the body will be identical, but Harris' experiments have shown that this general rule can be broken. By meddling with the hormones of his experimental animals, he negated the instructions of the genes.

The influence of environment upon growth seems relatively simple compared to that of hormones. A child who has no food will not grow, no matter what messages his body receives from genes and hormones. And a child's illnesses, his psychological state, subtle changes in the climate in which he lives—all these will affect his growth too, just as surely as lack of food.

During a war or an economic depression, but particularly during a war, an entire generation of children may exhibit slow or stunted growth because of the lack of food. Records were kept of children's growth in the German city of Stuttgart from 1911 to 1953. In the last years of World War II and the first few years after it, the average height of these children fell by more than an inch and not until 1953 did the average height of Stuttgart children rise to meet the level of children measured in 1939.

Slowed down by starvation

Also in postwar Germany, Elsie Widdowson and R. A. McCance of Cambridge University conducted a controlled growth study of some 160 orphans. All of these children lagged 10 to 20 months behind normal levels of growth and maturity, simply because they were not getting enough to eat. Their diet provided only about 80 per cent of the calories needed for the satisfactory nourishment of a growing child. For a year, Drs. Widdowson and McCance supplemented the children's diets with unlimited bread and other calorie-rich foods, such as jam, sugar, semolina. As might be expected, the children shot up in height and gained rapidly in weight, to become normal in both respects.

Were the children permanently damaged during the years when near-

A FAMOUS 18TH CENTURY GIANT, seven-foot seven-inch Charles Byrne toured England as a one-man sideshow. Later discovered to be the victim of a pituitary tumor, he attracted the attention of numerous surgeons, who connived to get his skeleton after he died. Though he was horrified at the idea, his bones in fact were preserved and are still on exhibit in London today.

135

starvation hampered their growth? Apparently not. Human beings have extraordinary recuperative powers. During a famine the human organism slows its growth rate and waits, as it were, for better times; it can make up the loss later if the famine does not last too long and is not too severe. Girls seem to resist malnutrition better than boys. Surveys in Guam, Hiroshima and elsewhere after World War II indicated a general retardation of growth, but all of them showed girls less retarded than boys. Similarly, the German girls studied by Drs. Widdowson and McCance returned to normal more quickly than the boys. Either the female is tougher than the male, or she uses her biological equipment more efficiently.

Other experiments conducted by Drs. Widdowson and McCance have thrown light upon the relation between emotional stress and growth. Most people would assume—and, as it turns out, assume rightly—that an unhappy child will not grow as fast as a happy one, all other things being equal. Normally, of course, "all other things" are very far from equal, and under normal circumstances the problem can hardly be attacked by science at all. But by using experimental and control groups (and partly by accident) Dr. Widdowson made observations that establish a clear connection between emotional states and growth.

The case of the cruel headmistress

Working with children in two orphanages—we can call them Orphanage A and Orphanage B—she chose a group of children from Orphanage A as experimental subjects. For six months she traced their growth on the orphanage diet, to establish their "normal" growth rate. Over the next six months, she supplemented their diet in the hope of producing a growth spurt. The children in Orphanage B, serving as control subjects, received no diet supplement at all. Theoretically, the two groups should have grown at about the same rate for the first six months; then the group in Orphanage A should have shot ahead. In fact, everything seemed to go wrong from the start. During the first six months, when both diets were unsupplemented, the children in Orphanage A gained more weight than the ones in Orphanage B. During the second six months, when the group in Orphanage A received diet supplements, they gained *less* weight than the group in Orphanage B.

The explanation, when it came, was simple enough. By coincidence, at the end of the first six-month period, a sternly disciplinarian headmistress had been transferred from Orphanage B to Orphanage A. She ruled the children rigidly at all times. What was worse, she chose mealtimes to administer public (and often unjustified) rebukes. Under her cruel charge, the growth rates of her tense, unhappy wards went down. And, unwittingly, she confirmed the researchers' conclusions in another

GROWTH HORMONE, a chemical secreted by the pituitary gland, was discovered by the American biologist H. M. Evans during the 1920s and '30s. The result of one of his many experiments, shown here, dramatizes the hormone's potent effect. The dachshund at left was given injections of pituitary extract from birth. In eight months he became a waddling 40-pounder—nearly twice as large as his untreated brother.

way. She had eight favorite children, whom she took with her from Orphanage B to Orphanage A. Even in Orphanage B, these teacher's pets had gained more weight than the other children; in Orphanage A, where they received diet supplements, they gained weight faster than ever. This made quite clear the link between emotional state and the rate of growth. Or as Dr. Widdowson put it, in an apt quotation: "Better a dinner of herbs where love is, than a stalled ox and hatred therewith."

In dealing with such environmental factors as food and psychological stress, science has done little more than confirm popular opinion. Elsewhere, as in the influence of climatic changes upon growth, science has come up with data for which it has no clear explanation, and which have no parallels in popular opinion. For example, on the average, growth in height proceeds faster in the spring than in other seasons. By contrast, gain in weight is fastest in the fall. In growing children and in adolescents, over half the annual gain in height occurs between the beginning of March and the end of August. The rate of gain in height in spring may be two to two and a half times greater than it is in autumn. On the other hand, two thirds of the annual gain in weight takes place between the beginning of September and the end of February. Weight may increase five times as much in the fall as it does in the spring. Some children actually lose weight in spring.

These figures, of course, are averages. Not every child shows such extreme differences, and it is interesting that well-nourished children seem to show them less than others. But the differences do exist, and they are generally substantial.

We can improve our environments—that is, we can provide better food, eliminate disease, reduce psychological strains. But we cannot much improve genetic and hormonal growth factors. Scientific techniques are not (and may never be) sufficiently refined to isolate and work upon the individual genes responsible for growth.

The growing American

The case for hormone manipulation is somewhat brighter. Children have been cured of dwarfism by injections of the pituitary growth hormone. Children with defective thyroid glands grow normally if they receive regular doses of thyroxine early enough. But boys and girls with genetic or hormonal abnormalities are relatively rare, while environmental improvements could better the growth of whole populations.

Almost every year, in fact, new evidence is turned up of the dramatic effects of better environments upon growth. In 1965, Albert Damon of the Department of Anthropology at Harvard University reported the results of a 30-year study of some 200 men living in the Boston area. Nearly all of them were born in the United States of Neapolitan parents, and all of them worked in the same factory. Those who were studied at the end of the research period averaged 2.1 inches taller than those who had been studied when the research began—a short-term increase of height that is the greatest ever recorded. The hereditary backgrounds of nearly all these men were the same. What had changed was their diet, their medical care, their living conditions.

In the long run, of course, improvements in environment can only permit individuals and populations to realize their maximum potential. The fact is highlighted by another study, this one conducted by Harry Bakwin and Sylvia McLaughlin. Comparing the heights of Harvard freshmen of the 1930s with those admitted in the late 1950s, they found significant differences between the growth trends of public-school and private-school graduates. Freshmen admitted to Harvard from public schools showed substantial height increases in the years covered by the study. Those admitted from private schools did not.

Why the difference? Because, argue Drs. Bakwin and McLaughlin, the environments of public-school boys improved substantially between the 1930s and the 1950s, while those of private-school boys remained much the same. Improved environments had finally permitted the boys from public schools to reach their maximum potential height; the boys from private schools had been reaching it all along.

The Body's Vital Chemicals

From conception to maturity, hormones play a vital role in growth. These chemical agents shape the growth of the child within the womb, stimulate the body's expansion from infancy to adolescence, bring about the transformation from adolescent into adult. In addition, hormones regularly prepare the bodies of women for the creation of a new organism. Some hormones act only on specific tissues. Others act throughout the body. Acting on the body at large, they also act on one another, regulating their output by a complex and sensitive feedback system. The hormones are secreted by the body's ductless, or endocrine, glands, the pituitary, thyroid, adrenals and gonads (opposite). During pregnancy, another, temporary source of hormones becomes operative in the form of the placenta, which serves as a sort of auxiliary endocrine gland, secreting substances that perform a vital role in the intricate physiology of mother and child.

SIX HORMONE FACTORIES
The glands most essential to growth are silhouetted within colored circles on the young runner opposite. The pituitary lies deep within the skull, the thyroid spreads across the front of the wind- pipe, the two adrenals cap the kidneys, the gonads are at the base of the torso. The pancreas, not shown here, plays no direct role in growth but influences it through the secretion of insulin.

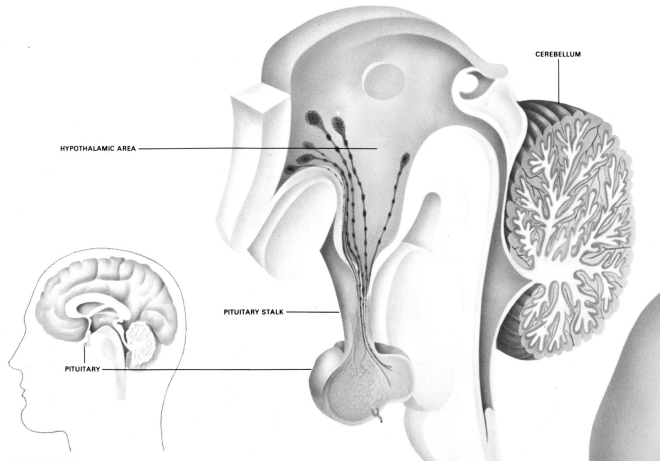

HYPOTHALAMIC AREA

CEREBELLUM

PITUITARY STALK

PITUITARY

ANTERIOR LOBE

A VITAL CENTER
Located at the base of the brain *(above, left)*, the pituitary gland is a small bulb about one third of an inch long. It is attached to the hypothalamus, an important region of the brain, by a short stalk and linked to it by a network of nerve fibers, blood vessels and other tissue *(above, right)*. The gland's anterior and posterior lobes secrete different kinds of hormones.

Command Post of the Endocrines

Of all the glands in the body's endocrine system, the pituitary is predominant. Its anterior lobe serves as a compact field headquarters for all gland action aimed at growth. (The posterior lobe's hormones do not influence the growth process.) Most of the anterior-lobe secretions are "trophic," meaning nourishing, hormones. They are transported throughout the body by the bloodstream, to their "target" glands, the thyroid, adrenals and gonads, where they stimulate hormone production. The pituitary gland not only issues orders, it also responds to the way those orders are carried out, boosting the output of trophic hormones when target glands lag, cutting back when their output is adequate *(page 142)*. The pituitary also secretes growth hormone, which acts directly on tissues to stimulate their growth.

Often called the body's master gland, the pituitary has a master of its own, the hypothalamus. This mass of nerve tissue is thought to determine the timing of various growth stages, such as adolescence, by stimulating the pituitary to secrete more or less of its several products. What controls the hypothalamus is not known. There is some evidence that it contains a built-in physiological clock which "knows" when the time has arrived for a boy to become a man.

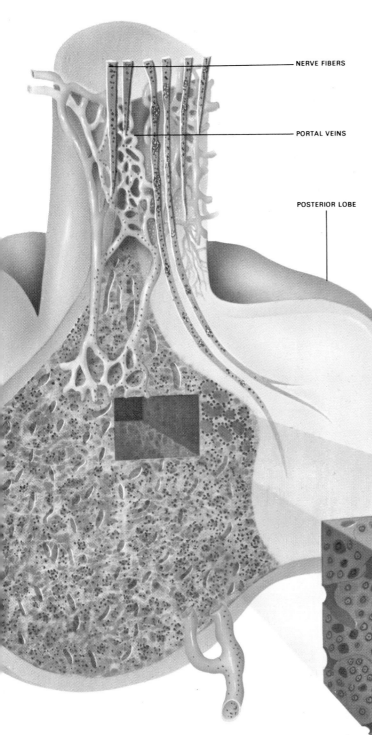

NERVE FIBERS

PORTAL VEINS

POSTERIOR LOBE

DETAIL OF
PORTAL VEINS
AND SECRETORY CELLS

ACTING ON ORDERS FROM ABOVE

An enlarged, cross-section view of the pituitary's anterior lobe *(left)* reveals the intricate connections between the gland and its governor, the hypothalamus. The small veins, or portal vessels, that supply blood to this lobe of the pituitary originate in the hypothalamus. Scientists suspect that hypothalamic nerves trigger the discharge of chemicals into these veins which prompt the gland to secrete particular hormones. The dye-stained section diagramed below shows the variety of cells that produce and contain the pituitary's diversified products.

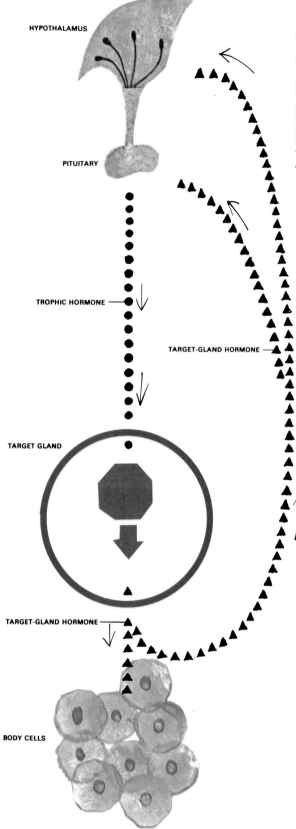

HYPOTHALAMUS

PITUITARY

TROPHIC HORMONE

TARGET-GLAND HORMONE

TARGET GLAND

TARGET-GLAND HORMONE

BODY CELLS

A GLANDULAR FEEDBACK SYSTEM

Like a furnace and its controlling thermostat, which produces more heat when the house gets too cool and less when the temperature warms up, the body's endocrines are a self-regulating system. Signals—trophic hormones *(black dots)* —from the pituitary thermostat stimulate a target gland, circled in red here and on subsequent pages. The target steps up production of its own hormones *(black triangles),* which act on body cells. Rising levels of these hormones feed back signals to the hypothalamus or the pituitary, cutting production of trophic hormones. The feedback mechanism keeps the production of these potent chemicals under tight control.

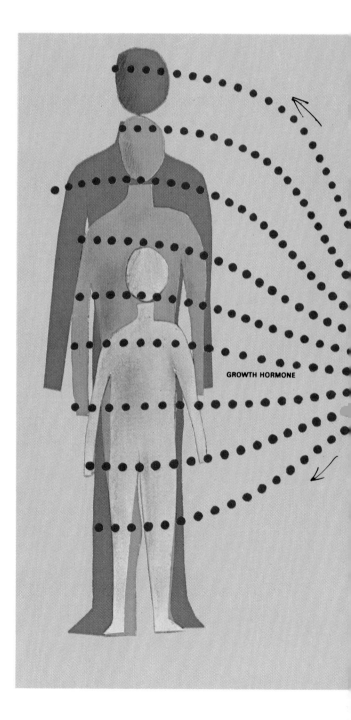

GROWTH HORMONE

Hormone Action in Childhood

In the preadolescent years, growth is mainly a matter of building up a sturdy skeleton, laying down tissues and expanding the brain. Two hormones are chiefly responsible for stimulating this development. Somatotrophin, commonly known as growth hormone, is one of them. Produced by the pituitary, it stimulates the growth of bones and the production of proteins (it also influences other metabolic processes less concerned in growth). Somatotrophin is assisted by other hormones, especially that secreted by the thyroid gland. Without the presence of this substance, growth hormone is partially inactive. Thyroid hormone itself directly stimulates the growth of certain organs (below) and may possibly play a part in maintaining proper proportions in the growing body as well. Like growth hormone, the thyroid hormone also influences the body in ways less directly related to growth. In particular, its concentration in the blood determines the rate at which the body metabolizes food and produces energy.

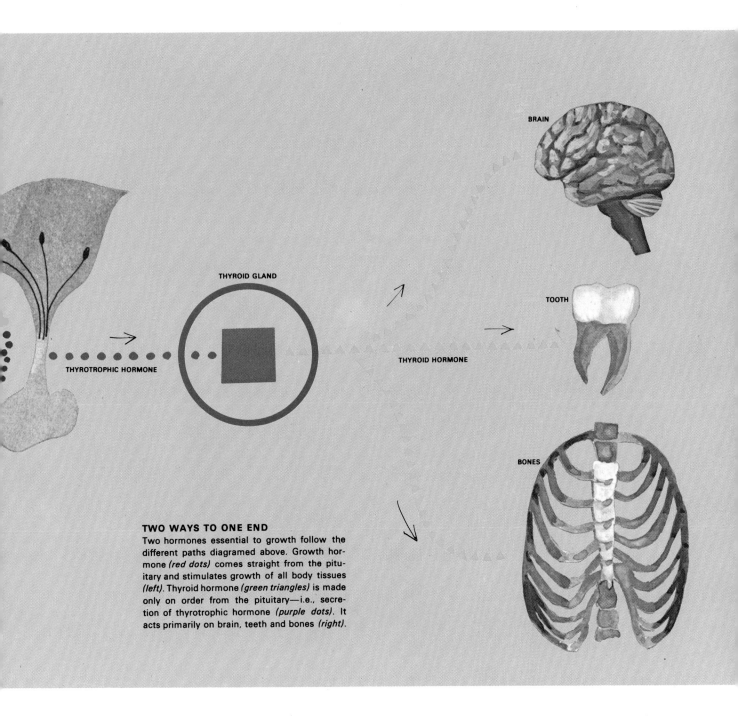

BRAIN

THYROID GLAND

TOOTH

THYROTROPHIC HORMONE

THYROID HORMONE

BONES

TWO WAYS TO ONE END
Two hormones essential to growth follow the different paths diagramed above. Growth hormone *(red dots)* comes straight from the pituitary and stimulates growth of all body tissues *(left)*. Thyroid hormone *(green triangles)* is made only on order from the pituitary—i.e., secretion of thyrotrophic hormone *(purple dots)*. It acts primarily on brain, teeth and bones *(right)*.

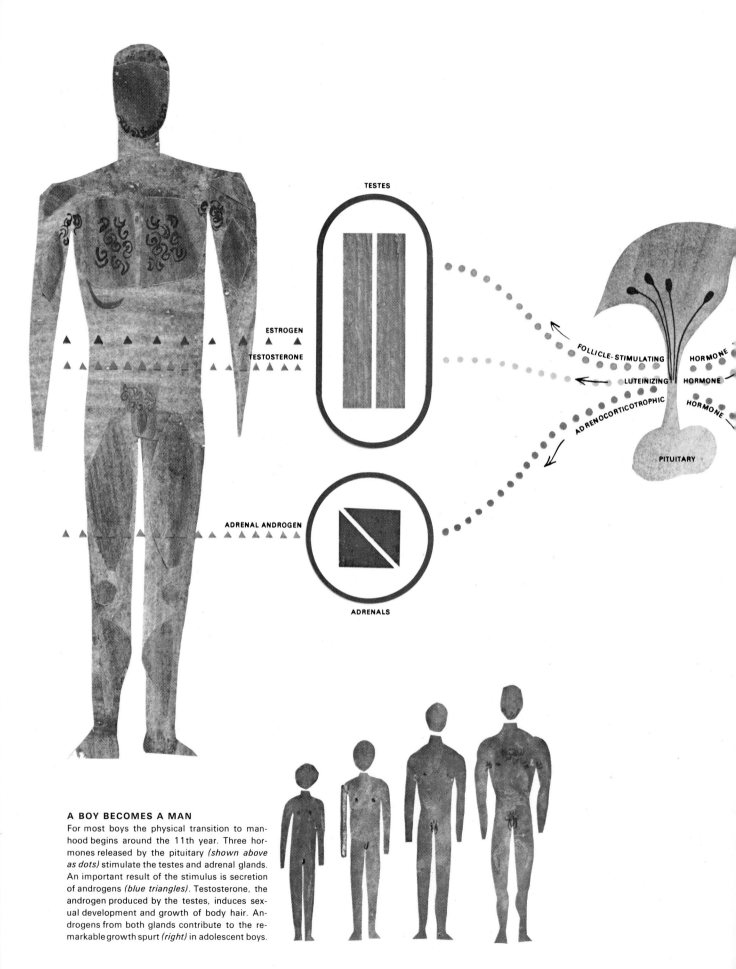

TESTES

ESTROGEN

TESTOSTERONE

ADRENAL ANDROGEN

ADRENALS

FOLLICLE-STIMULATING

HORMONE

LUTEINIZING HORMONE

ADRENOCORTICOTROPHIC HORMONE

PITUITARY

A BOY BECOMES A MAN

For most boys the physical transition to manhood begins around the 11th year. Three hormones released by the pituitary *(shown above as dots)* stimulate the testes and adrenal glands. An important result of the stimulus is secretion of androgens *(blue triangles)*. Testosterone, the androgen produced by the testes, induces sexual development and growth of body hair. Androgens from both glands contribute to the remarkable growth spurt *(right)* in adolescent boys.

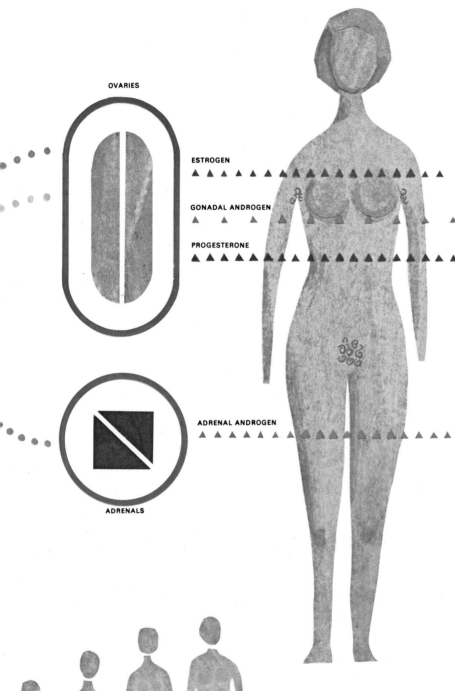

OVARIES

ESTROGEN

▲ ▲ ▲ ▲ ▲ ▲ ▲ ▲ ▲ ▲ ▲ ▲ ▲ ▲ ▲ ▲ ▲

GONADAL ANDROGEN

▲ ▲ ▲ ▲

PROGESTERONE

▲ ▲ ▲ ▲ ▲ ▲ ▲ ▲ ▲ ▲ ▲ ▲ ▲

ADRENAL ANDROGEN

▲ ▲ ▲ ▲ ▲ ▲ ▲ ▲ ▲ ▲ ▲ ▲

ADRENALS

The Hormones in Adolescence

The major changes of adolescence, sexual maturation and accelerated growth, are both brought about by marked changes in hormone secretions. In both sexes, the process, schematically diagramed on these pages, begins when the hypothalamus signals the pituitary to take up a new role. The pituitary thereupon begins putting out two new trophic hormones—curiously, they are the same in both sexes—that stimulate the gonads, which have been almost inactive since before birth. The adrenals' activity also rises.

At this point, the process diverges in the two sexes. In boys, both trophic hormones spark the growth of cells that will produce spermatozoa; one also stimulates other cells to produce the male sex hormone, testosterone. In girls, the process is different. Egg-cell production also requires the efforts of both trophic hormones, but the apparatus that matures the eggs produces not one but two sex hormones, estrogen and progesterone, at different stages in its cycle. While each sex has its own distinctive sex hormones, each also produces small amounts of the other sex's hormones.

A GIRL BECOMES A WOMAN
Development into womanhood is triggered by pituitary hormones at about age nine. Under their stimulus the adrenals and ovaries secrete androgens *(blue triangles above)*, which quicken growth *(left)* just as they do in boys. The ovaries also secrete estrogen; this substance stimulates the development of the breasts and of the rounded female form. It may also be a factor in terminating growth earlier in girls, by hastening complete ossification of the long bones.

The Complexities of Womanhood

Every 28 days or so, a woman's body prepares itself for the growth of a new organism. Except during pregnancy, this cyclical process *(right)* repeats itself regularly for about 35 years after puberty. It is controlled by one of the body's most intricate feedback systems, in which four hormones enter and exit, advance and retreat, like performers in a classical ballet. Each hormone presides over one step in the process, and in addition triggers the next step.

The sequence begins with the pituitary's secretion of follicle-stimulating hormone (FSH). This causes the Graafian follicle in the ovary to grow and secrete the hormone estrogen. The estrogen cuts back the pituitary's production of FSH and sets it to making luteinizing hormone (LH). This in turn triggers the follicle to release its ovum and to evolve into the *corpus luteum,* which secretes progesterone (and a little estrogen). The new hormone prepares the uterus to receive the egg if it is fertilized and also cuts LH production. If fertilization does not occur, production of both estrogen and progesterone drops. This causes the uterine lining to slough away and permits FSH production to start, beginning the cycle once more. If the egg is fertilized, however, a fifth hormone joins the cast and the plot changes *(far right).*

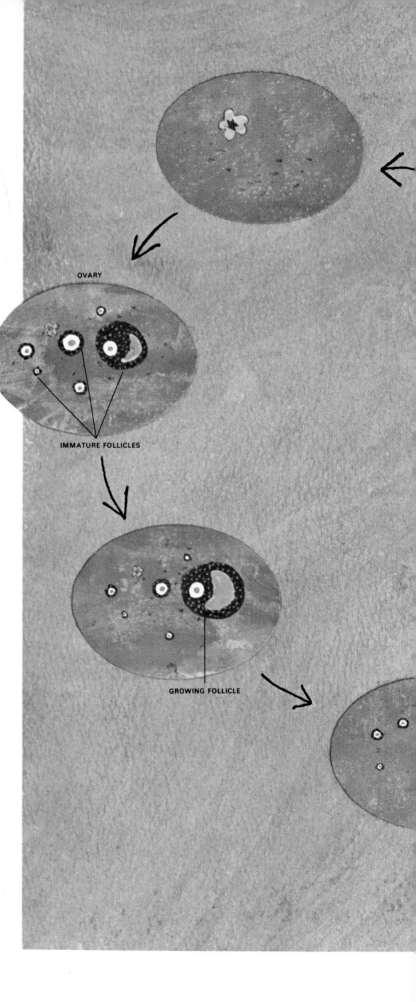

OVARY

IMMATURE FOLLICLES

GROWING FOLLICLE

CORPUS LUTEUM OF PREGNANCY

THE BEGINNING

When the clump of cells from the fertilized ovum implants itself in the uterus *(below, white mass)*, it soon secretes a new hormone *(squares)*. This causes the *corpus luteum (above)* to produce more estrogen as well as progesterone. Without these, pregnancy could not continue.

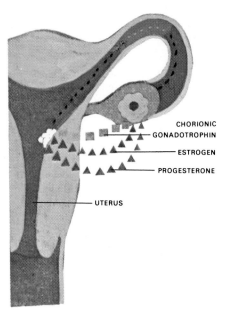

CHORIONIC
GONADOTROPHIN

ESTROGEN

PROGESTERONE

UTERUS

CORPUS LUTEUM

OVUM

RUPTURED FOLLICLE

'URE FOLLICLE

A CYCLE OF PREPARATION

Within the ovary, the monthly cycle begins *(left center)* when an ovum-containing follicle, stimulated by FSH, starts to grow. As it enlarges, it pushes toward the ovary surface *(bottom)*. When the mature ovum, ready for fertilization, breaks out of the follicle to leave the ovary, cells of the former follicle are transformed into the *corpus luteum (right, center)*. At this point there are two possibilities. If the ovum is fertilized, the *corpus luteum* will remain and grow. If not, it will shrink and degenerate as the monthly cycle ends.

147

Hormones That Shape a New Being

During the growth of an embryo from a cluster of cells to a baby, the complexities of hormonal action reach a peak. Involved are the mother's endocrine system, the gradually maturing glands of the embryo and also the placenta. The placenta, which serves the embryo as a sort of combined lung, liver, kidney and intestine, secretes hormones as well.

By the third month of pregnancy, the corpus luteum in the ovary atrophies as the placenta takes over the job of supplying estrogen and progesterone. For this purpose it absorbs incomplete hormones of various sorts from adrenal glands of the mother and the budding adrenals of the fetus, and transforms them into usable ones. The finished products are important to both mother and baby. In the fetus, estrogen stimulates sexual development, assisted in male babies (shown here) by a male hormone from the fetal testes. In the mother, estrogen prepares the breasts for nursing. Progesterone serves as a semiprocessed material for the immature fetal adrenals, which convert it into adrenocortical hormones. It also promotes changes in the mother's uterus to accommodate the growing baby.

● PITUITARY

● THYROID

● ADRENALS

● OVARIES

PLACENTA, MOTHER AND BABY
During pregnancy a woman's endocrine system *(above)* operates in a special way. Her pituitary continues to stimulate the thyroid and adrenals to produce their normal hormones, some of which are used by the child as well as the mother. The ovaries, however, are quiescent. Estrogen and progesterone secreted by the placenta *(right)* prevent the pituitary from making the hormones that would quicken the ovaries into action. The placenta's hormone factories are its syncytial cells, lining the villi where materials are exchanged between mother and child.

PLACENTA

FETAL ARTERIES
FETAL VEIN

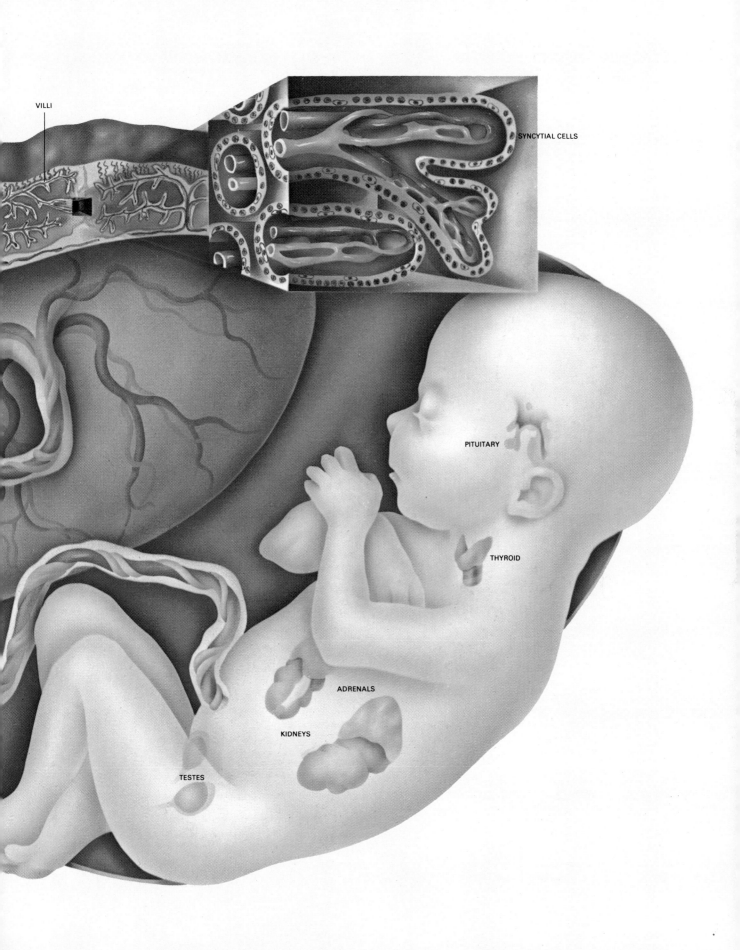

VILLI

SYNCYTIAL CELLS

PITUITARY

THYROID

ADRENALS

KIDNEYS

TESTES

7
Flaws in Development

THE HUMAN BODY is far more intricate than the most sophisticated products of man's technology. A giant computer or a space rocket embodies millions of skilled man-hours, yet neither encompasses the multitude of different parts or the manifold possibilities of one small baby. If an engineer were ordered to devise a reliable process for manufacturing so elaborate a structure by the millions, he would quickly take to tranquilizers. Yet the human growth process, despite its almost unimaginable complexity, works perfectly most of the time. If it did not, *Homo sapiens* might degenerate into a race of monsters and might soon become extinct. When growth does go awry, it creates a giant or a dwarf, a child with six fingers or one with two heads, an albino or a hemophiliac—or worse.

The overwhelming majority of aberrations occur, or begin to occur, before birth. Once a child is safely born, only a catastrophe can seriously distort the growth process. Malnutrition or severe illness can temporarily or even permanently flatten the growth curve, but can seldom do more than that. The few serious aberrations that originate after birth, such as some of the cases of sexual precocity described earlier, are caused for the most part by disorders of the endocrine glands.

The embryo is far more vulnerable to noxious influences. An infectious or toxic agent can interfere with it, or it may suffer from defective genes. The result in either case is apt to be one of the many aberrations summed up in the phrase, congenital defects. These words cover one of the largest, loosest and certainly most tragic categories of disorders that afflict man. Most conspicuous are the gross malformations that have given the words their grim aura: Siamese twins; hydrocephalics, with distended heads; anencephalics, without brains; people with a missing limb, a harelip or a clubfoot. Malformations of this sort have shocked and fascinated men since the Stone Age, when shamans drew pictures of two-headed creatures on the walls of caves. Clay tablets from Mesopotamia describe in detail deformities of the ears, nose, mouth, sex organs and limbs. Historians believe that the Babylonians took congenital defects as profound omens and kept these records with the aim of divining the future.

Over a thousand different defects, ranging from monstrosities to color blindness, have been catalogued, and nobody pretends that the list is complete. Any tissue from skin to bone, any organ from heart to kidney, any function from the manufacture of a vital enzyme to the synthesis of hair and skin pigment may be defective.

One of the few things that can be said collectively about this heterogeneous group of disorders is that it takes an enormous toll of human life and human potential. No worldwide statistics have been compiled, and projections based on small-scale studies are misleading because the

A VICTIM OF THALIDOMIDE
Like thousands of other unfortunate children, this boy is a victim of thalidomide, a sedative his mother took in her second month of pregnancy—the crucial period when the growing embryo is especially vulnerable. Luckily, the drug does not seem to affect the brain; with therapy and the help of artificial limbs, most thalidomide babies will lead nearly normal lives.

figures vary widely and inexplicably from race to race and region to region. For example, whites suffer from anencephaly seven times as frequently as Negroes, while Negroes are seven times as apt to be born with extra fingers. Even in the U.S., a country abundantly supplied with vital statistics, figures on growth aberrations contain a large component of guesswork. Many defective embryos are lost through spontaneous abortions early in pregnancy, but these are seldom recorded. Furthermore, many defects are difficult to spot at birth, and some emerge only after many years. A man born with a defective gene may begin to develop in his forties the symptoms of speech disturbance and mental deterioration that characterize the degenerative disease of the nervous system known as Huntington's chorea.

Some startling figures

The incomplete statistics that are available show that the problem is serious. In 1946, Columbia-Presbyterian Medical Center carried out a study of nearly 6,000 pregnancies from the fourth month of fetal life through the first year after birth, tabulating all the malformations and congenital diseases that turned up. Of the infants born alive, about 4 per cent, or one in 25, had suffered serious disorders ranging from heart defects to mental retardation. A slightly smaller percentage showed mild defects. If these proportions hold for the general population, about 160,000 seriously defective children are born in the U.S. every year. Understanding, preventing and treating birth defects are thus urgent matters.

Researchers now look for the causes of birth defects in three general areas: defective genes, abnormal arrangements of the chromosomes and unfavorable factors occurring in the baby's uterine environment during pregnancy.

One of the subtlest gene defects, and also one of the first to be fully understood and effectively controlled, is a type of severe retardation now called phenylketonuria, or PKU. The control of PKU dates from the day in 1934 when a Norwegian physician, Asbjørn Følling, was visited by a mother and her two retarded children. The woman had noticed a peculiar musty odor clinging to both children, and asked Følling if the odor had anything to do with the youngsters' being retarded. In the course of his examination, Følling tested the children's urine and found a peculiar substance in it. After lengthy analysis, he identified the substance as a chemical relative of phenylalanine, a common compound present in almost every protein that man consumes, including mother's milk. With this clue, he and researchers in other countries were able to identify the cause of the retardation as a defect in body chemistry. In PKU victims, the enzyme that normally metabolizes phenylalanine

SIAMESE TWINS were observed as early as the 16th Century when these engravings were done by the Swiss physician Jacobus Rueff. Like many of his contemporaries, Rueff believed that malformations of this sort were manifestations of divine punishment.

is defective in its structure. Undigested phenylalanine accumulates in the tissues, giving the urine and sweat a peculiar odor. The phenylalanine increases with every meal to the point where it and its by-products injure the brain.

Because physicians could not repair the defective enzyme, they sought to counter its effects by providing its victims with a diet containing a minimum of phenylalanine. This could be done only by tampering with the protein content of their food—and it was not easy. During the first major attempt, in England soon after World War II, workers laboriously processed food for a three-year-old girl victim. Even so, they were barely able to finish each batch by mealtime. Physicians watched eagerly as the accumulated poisons disappeared from her tissues, but the result was discouraging. Though the child did in fact become more alert, she remained retarded. The damage already done to her brain cells was irreversible. Clearly, PKU infants had to be identified and treated as early as possible.

The first effort in this direction was the "diaper test." At three to four weeks a PKU baby's urine is detectably abnormal. A little ferric chloride dropped on his wet diaper forms a blue-green ring. But detection at even three to four weeks was sometimes too late.

Finally, in 1961 a young American doctor, Robert Guthrie, developed a much more sensitive blood test that reveals the defect when the baby is only a few days old. PKU victims can be started on the necessary diet before any significant amount of phenylalanine has accumulated in their systems and while the brains are still normal. By the age of five or so, when the important period of brain growth has ended, they can generally eat ordinary foods. Many U.S. hospitals now routinely use this test on all babies, and in several states it is mandatory.

Once researchers were able to identify PKU, and distinguish it from other kinds of mental retardation, they soon discovered another important fact about it: it runs in families. From the way it is inherited, they have concluded that it results from a single defective gene. Those who inherit this gene from both parents are normal before birth, except for one defective liver enzyme. But this seemingly trivial defect can warp the entire mental development of the child.

Major ills from minor causes

Most hereditary birth defects, it is now believed, stem from equally minute causes. In a few cases, the specific chemical defect is known. In sickle-cell anemia, a blood disorder, it has been pinpointed even more precisely: alteration of a single link in the long chain molecule of hemoglobin, the protein that carries oxygen in the bloodstream. The chemical basis of most hereditary disorders, however, is still uncertain.

CHANG AND ENG were the conjoined twins from Siam who became so world-famous in the 19th Century in exhibitions that persons similarly afflicted were afterward called "Siamese twins." They settled in the U.S., married and fathered 11 normal children.

Hereditary defects include glandular disorders such as cystic fibrosis, which causes the production of an abnormally thick, gluey mucus that blocks the lung's air passages and also prevents essential digestive enzymes from leaving the pancreas. Others are defects ranging from minor anomalies—harelip, cleft palate and extra fingers, all of which can be repaired by plastic surgery—to irreparable conditions such as a malformation of the inner ear that causes congenital deafness. Because they can be inherited, they must involve genes that supply faulty patterns for some of the body's chemical operations. But the precise operations and enzymes involved are still unknown.

Scrambled instructions

Not all genetic defects are inherited. In some embryos the hereditary instructions that govern growth are initially all present and correct, but these instructions become garbled as they are passed from one cell to another during the process of cell division. Mishaps of this sort usually involve not a single defective gene but a sweeping rearrangement of the cell's genetic material. Not surprisingly, the resulting defects are usually grave.

The true nature of these disorders has been ascertained only since 1956, with the development of techniques to make accurate observations of human chromosomes. Then it became possible not only to count the chromosomes (the normal number is 46) but also to identify each of the 23 pairs of chromosomes contained in human cells. During the growing embryo's repeated cell divisions, the chromosome pairs constantly split and separate, operating with the orderly precision of a crack drill team. But it happens that some chromosomes get out of step. Three French scientists in 1959 examined cells from children with a very serious growth disorder called Mongolism, or Down's disease. They found 47 chromosomes instead of 46. Since then many patients with this condition have been examined, and an extra chromosome has usually showed up in their cells. Its presence is disastrous. Though those who have it often appear normal at birth, their growth is already badly deranged. Many victims of Down's disease are born with heart disorders and lacking nose bones or teeth. All of them quickly develop curiously broad faces with flat, low-bridged noses and skin folds over the eyes. All are mentally retarded, most of them seriously.

Soon after this discovery of a disorder linked to a chromosomal aberration, several others turned up. Most of them involved too many or too few of the chromosomes that determine sex. Normal females have two sex chromosomes that are known as X chromosomes; normal males receive one X chromosome from the mother, and a smaller Y chromosome from the father. The aberrations found in sex chromosomes

A MEDICAL MISNOMER, the term "Mongolism" was popularly applied to a serious congenital growth disorder on the assumption that a peculiarity of eye development that resulted from the malady (correctly known as Down's disease) made "Mongoloids'" eyes similar to those of Mongolians. The so-called "Mongoloid" child has a skin fold in the corner of the eye *(far right)*. Actually, the eye of a Mongolian is distinguished by a curved, overlapping eyelid *(center)*. Except for the fold, the eye of the child with Down's disease is formed in the same way as any European's *(left)*.

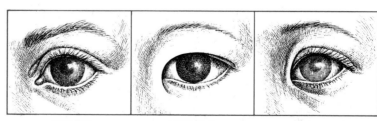

EUROPEAN   MONGOLIAN   DOWN'S DISEASE

suggest the almost unlimited possibilities of error in the chromosomes' elaborate maneuvers during cell division. Females have been found with only one chromosome or with three; males, instead of the normal XY pattern, may have XXY, XYY, or even XXXXY. Some of these chromosomal anomalies produce serious derangements of development, and a few have been blamed for personality abnormalities. One result is often infertility, but many women who have three X chromosomes are fertile and apparently normal in other respects. Indeed, many three-X-chromosome cases are believed to go undetected.

Study of chromosome problems indicates that the replication and division of chromosomes can go wrong at any stage. In some cases the mistake occurs even before conception, in the parent's sex cells. A chromosome may break in two and one of the fragments become permanently attached to another chromosome. Or the division may be uneven, giving too many chromosomes to one cell, too few to another. Aberrations can also occur during embryonic development. Some people have been found to have two different kinds of cells in their bodies, one with normal chromosomes and one without. In these so-called "mosaic" individuals, the original egg cell must have been normal. The defect was created at some later stage in the process of cell division. In one case of this sort, a boy with body characteristics associated with Down's disease but with a normal I.Q. was found to have skin cells containing an extra chromosome, but with a normal complement of chromosomes in his blood cells.

The abnormal victims of chromosomal troubles provide investigators with their best opportunity for "mapping" chromosomes—that is, for discovering which chromosomes govern which areas of growth. For example, victims of Down's disease are known to develop leukemia—excess production of white blood cells—more than three times as often as normal people. This may be related to their chromosomal abnormality. Some leukemia patients have been found to have a defect in one of the chromosomes known to be involved in Down's disease: it is smaller than normal, perhaps because a bit has broken off and become lost. It seems likely that some of the genes in this chromosome are concerned with the production of white blood cells.

Influences within and without

Only about 40 per cent of birth defects can be definitely classified as either hereditary or environmental. Hereditary factors, including defective genes and aberrant chromosomes, account for about half of these. The other 20 per cent result from external agents that act on the embryo during its long, slow process of maturation in the womb.

Experimenters in embryology have learned how to induce birth defects in animals by subjecting the mother to radiation, vitamin deficiency or inadequate oxygen. Not surprisingly, they found that the earlier the mother was subjected to such damage, the worse the defect. Anything that attacks an embryo when its cells are relatively few in number is almost bound to wreak havoc. To show that prenatal influences could produce birth defects in the laboratory, however, did not prove that it happened in real life. That proof came in 1940, when Australia was hit by the most severe epidemic of German measles it had ever known. Since the disease is a mild one, the victims showed no immediate aftereffects. By the end of the year, the birth of defective babies in alarming numbers was noted. Some were stillborn. Many of those that survived had the horrifying multiple defects that pointed to damage during the first, most vulnerable months: they were blinded by cataracts, they were deaf, they had malformed hearts and were retarded. Altogether, some 350 defective infants were born. And nearly all of these were born to women who had contracted German measles seven to eight months before. Since then, studies by embryologists and pediatricians have identified the German-measles virus as the culprit. About 50 per cent of mothers who have German measles during the first month of pregnancy will bear a defective child.

Any viral infection during early pregnancy is now considered suspect. Mumps and influenza have come under particularly strong suspicion, but not enough evidence has yet been gathered to label them as definitive dangers. And strenuous measures have been taken to prevent the damage caused by German measles. Since doctors have not yet developed a vaccine for the infection, pregnant women are urged to avoid exposure to it. Those who are infected are treated with gamma globulin, which reduces the effects of the virus on the mother and, it is hoped, on the child.

The danger of radiation

Radiation, long known to cause congenital defects in animals, came under increasing suspicion in human cases after World War II. Fifteen pregnant Japanese women who had been within a mile and a half of the Hiroshima atom-bomb explosion produced babies with damaged skulls and brains. In the U.S. and in Britain the malformed brains and eyes of some babies have been linked to heavy doses of X-rays which their mothers received during pregnancy. The connection between the irradiation and the defects is still not clear, but physicians now use X-rays on pregnant women only for the most compelling reasons.

Only a few years ago, a historic disaster added drugs to the list of factors that cause dangers during pregnancy. In 1960, physicians in West Germany began noticing an unusual increase of birth defects of one particular type. The babies suffered from phocomelia (from the Greek words *phoke*, a seal, and *melos*, a limb). These children were born with seal-like, abbreviated limbs, somewhat resembling flippers. In the 10 years before 1959, only 15 cases of phocomelia had been recorded in all West Germany. But in 1960, 19 seal babies were born in the city of Bonn alone, 27 in Münster, 46 in Hamburg. By the end of the outbreak in 1961, the total had reached several hundred.

A sinister sedative

Toward the end of 1961 a persistent West German pediatrician, Dr. Widukind Lenz, began querying the mothers of seal babies and their attending physicians, asking them to search their memories for everything that had happened during pregnancy, including anything the women had eaten or drunk. Many of them recalled taking a sleeping pill that contained a newly developed sedative called thalidomide. The drug seemed an ideal one. It had no serious side effects, was completely nonaddictive and remarkably safe. More than 100 people had tried to commit suicide with thalidomide pills and failed. Because West Germany had few restrictions on the sale of new drugs, thalidomide was being distributed not only in the form of sleeping pills but also as an ingredient in cough syrups and cold cures. It was often recommended for the morning sickness of early pregnancy.

By the time Lenz had tracked down thalidomide as the villain in the case of the seal babies, its use had spread from Germany to other European countries as well as to Canada, South America, Japan and the Near East. In November 1961 the German manufacturer stopped production, but the total of thalidomide babies ultimately passed 5,000 in West Germany and at least 1,000 in other countries.

American mothers were spared the thalidomide disaster through the suspicions of Frances Kelsey, a doctor in the U.S. Food and Drug Administration. An American drug firm had applied for permission to distribute the drug in this country, but Dr. Kelsey repeatedly refused to approve the application until she had conclusive evidence of its safety. When the West German tragedy became known, the manufacturers withdrew the application. Meanwhile, however, they had already sent out some thousands of free samples to physicians. Fortunately, few got into the hands of pregnant women: American thalidomide babies numbered less than half a dozen, and most of these were the victims of pills brought in from Europe.

The thalidomide disaster shocked people all over the world. Drug-control laws were tightened in many countries, including the U.S. Subsequently, other drugs besides thalidomide were found to damage fetuses. They include certain hormones as well as anticancer and anti-

COURT CURIOSITIES, two dwarfs accompany the Italian duke Cosimo I de Medici in a 16th Century engraving. Regarded as funny freaks endowed with special talents, dwarfs were often kept as servants or jesters by the nobility. This practice went out of fashion in the 18th Century, when a more compassionate attitude on deformity spread.

malarial agents. Physicians still prescribe these substances, but not to women in their childbearing years.

The fact that hormonal medication during pregnancy can warp the growth of the embryo obviously raises the question of whether a disorder of the mother's own hormones might have the same effect. Observations of mothers with certain tumors that secrete hormonelike substances suggest that it can. This finding has in a sense brought the study of maternal influences full circle. Some researchers are now taking a second—and serious—look at the old mother-was-frightened-by-a-cow superstition that maternal impressions can influence the embryo's normal development. Serious psychological stress, they point out, can profoundly alter the mother's hormone output, perhaps to the point where the growing baby will be affected.

Research in this and other areas may yet dispel the cloud of uncertainty that still surrounds congenital defects. Physicians can prevent some of these disorders by protecting pregnant women from dangerous drugs or X-rays. In a few cases, like PKU, they can mitigate or eliminate the impact of faulty body chemistry on growth. Surgeons can repair cleft palates and remove extra fingers. In recent years, they have even repaired many defective hearts. For the majority of birth defects, however, a cure, let alone prevention, is still in the future.

When the Pituitary Malfunctions

In some human beings that most important growth-controlling gland, the pituitary, functions abnormally. The results are startling, often tragic. The two extremes of human stature are giantism and dwarfism, and while other factors are sometimes involved, the usual cause for these abnormalities is the production by the pituitary of too much or too little of its growth hormone. Counteracting these effects is difficult, partly because of the inaccessibility of the gland situated in the skull. Only recently have surgical and radiation-treatment techniques improved enough to assure some success in damping hyperactive pituitary glands. Dwarfism too can now be controlled by injections of growth hormone. But there is a critical shortage of natural human growth hormone (HGH) available for such treatment. As a step toward making it synthetically, scientists are now trying to untangle the hormone's complex chemical structure.

THE LONG AND THE SHORT OF GROWTH
Extremes of growth caused by too little pituitary secretion of the growth hormone *(left)* and too much *(right)* are exhibited by two men who, curiously, are brothers-in-law. The dwarf stands just three feet high, while the giant measures a towering seven foot eight inches. For some reason, pituitary-caused dwarfism is much more common than the reverse—pituitary giantism.

Giantism and Acromegaly

An oversupply of pituitary growth hormone—hyperpituitarism—can result in two conditions: if it occurs during the growing years, the result is giantism, which produces an individual of enormous proportions. In cases of this sort, excessive growth is usually concentrated chiefly in the head and lower extremities.

When it strikes a person whose overall growth has been completed, hyperpituitarism causes acromegaly. The chief symptom of this disease is the enlargement of various parts of the body, most notably the head, hands and feet, accompanied by lethargy and severe headaches. Doctors are divided as to the right treatment for acromegaly, but two methods are most usual: surgical removal of the pituitary, and the use of radiation to slow its activity. This can involve planting radioactive material right in the gland or assaulting it with a powerful stream of radiation *(opposite)*.

THE "ALTON GIANT"

Towering over his 5'11" father, Robert Wadlow, 20, stood 8'10¾" and wore size 37 shoes when photographed here in 1939. Called the "Alton Giant" after his Illinois hometown, he died at 22 from the effects of a minor injury.

THE RAVAGES OF ACROMEGALY

In 1892 this young man *(left)* weighed 140 pounds. Then he developed acromegaly. By 1910 *(right)* his face had become malformed and he weighed 200 pounds. Doctors, ignorant of the problem, gave him pituitary extract instead of trying to cut down his pituitary activity.

AN ANTIPITUITARY WEAPON
Wearing a plastic helmet that holds her head in the right position, an acromegalic patient is bombarded by a beam of atomic particles from a cyclotron. This installation at the University of California directs the radiation beam so accurately that only the pituitary gland is affected.

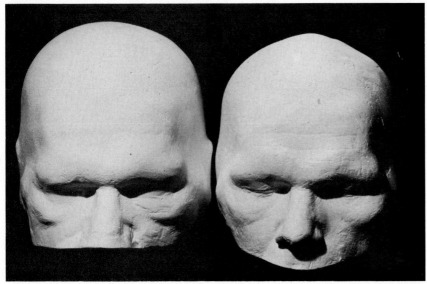

REPAIRING THE DAMAGE
Two plaster casts of an acromegalic patient's head, made five years apart, show the beneficial effect of radiation treatment of the pituitary. After repeated treatments curbed the production of growth hormone, the overgrowth of the skull at the left was markedly diminished.

The Case of the Boy Who Could Not Grow

At nine months, Frank was a normal-sized baby.

Brother Earl at 2 was as tall as Frank at 4.

Mr. Hooey and Earl, 14, tower over Frank at 16.

Though dwarfism of various kinds appears to be as old as man, it was not possible until recently to distinguish pituitary dwarfs from other types. The pituitary dwarf, though his size is obviously diminutive, is in most other respects a perfectly formed human being—such as the young Canadian Frank Hooey *(opposite)*. The first child of Mr. and Mrs. Alex Hooey, Frank appeared at birth to be a normal infant. But it soon became apparent that his rate of growth was far behind schedule, and by the time he reached 17, he was only 4'3" —the height of an average eight-and-a-half-year-old.

His parents had tried everything. A host of specialists had treated him, with no results. But in 1958 he was directed to Dr. M. S. Raben, a pioneer endocrinologist who was getting exciting results by stimulating growth with human growth hormone—HGH —which had been extracted from the pituitary glands of deceased donors. For the results of Frank's treatment by Dr. Raben, turn to the next page.

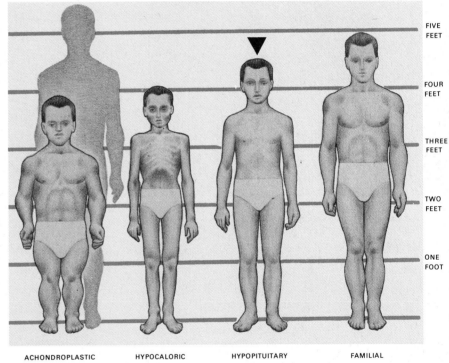

ACHONDROPLASTIC   HYPOCALORIC   HYPOPITUITARY   FAMILIAL

FIVE FEET
FOUR FEET
THREE FEET
TWO FEET
ONE FOOT

A COLLECTION OF DWARFS
Of the four types of dwarfs (charted above at age 18, with a normal individual shadowed in background), science currently can offer substantial help only to the one with insufficient pituitary growth hormone *(arrow)*. The achondroplastic was deformed before birth; the hypocaloric was stunted by malnutrition, and the familial irrevocably inherited his small stature.

THE SMALLEST CADET
At 15, Frank was the smallest cadet ever to attend Royal Canadian Air Force camp. Here he gamely poses with a six-foot sergeant who stands nearly 20 inches taller. Frank was a bright and spunky boy and, unlike many pituitary dwarfs, even participated in several team sports.

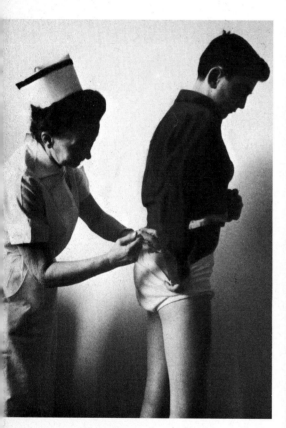

FOR RENEWED GROWTH
Frank receives his thrice-weekly injection of three milligrams of HGH. Dr. Raben started Frank's treatment by giving him other hormones for eight months, then putting him on HGH when he did not respond. Later, testosterone was added to speed final stages of maturity.

MARKING UP THE RESULTS
Mr. and Mrs. Hooey proudly record their son's new height on the kitchen doorway. Here, at age 23, he stands 5'6½", below average but well within the normal range. The black mark behind his shoulder indicates his height five years earlier, before he started HGH treatment.

A New Life from New Growth

After five years of treatment with HGH—under the supervision of Dr. Raben—Frank has been transformed from a pituitary dwarf *(previous page)* into a young man of normal size. Had he been born a few years earlier, he would have been doomed to a lifetime of looking up at his peers. Fortunately, the skeletons of pituitary dwarfs do not harden at the normal age, so it was possible for Frank to grow at an age when most adolescents have almost stopped.

Pituitary dwarfism is at first rather difficult to diagnose. Moreover, not enough is yet known about the reaction of the body to HGH to be certain of the best time to begin treatment.

There are probably about 5,000 pituitary dwarfs in America, many of whom could benefit greatly from HGH. But the supply is lamentably low, since it can be obtained only from glands removed at death. Virtually every pituitary, even from aged or diseased donors, contains HGH—but only enough for a few days' treatment. For a truly sufficient supply, glands should be obtained from at least three fourths of the 1.8 million who die annually in the U.S. In fact only about 50,000 are collected—enough for research but far too little to treat all those who need it.

A HIGH-STANDING BOWLER
Frank discusses a fine point of a game he likes with his teammates and his youngest brother *(far right)*. Frank's rapid growth did not sap his strength, nor did it interfere with his coordination. He rolls a hefty 16-pound ball with near-professional skill, and has won a first-place trophy in a men's major-league bowling competition. He also is fond of dancing and ice skating.

Costlier than Gold Dust

Dr. Maurice Raben began his first successful treatment of hypopituitary dwarfs with injections of the human growth hormone in 1956. Since that time, more than 100 dwarfs have been treated and their growth successfully stimulated. Working in his laboratory at the Tufts New England Medical Center, Dr. Raben and his staff extract the hormone from human pituitary glands obtained from the U.S. and 15 foreign countries. They use an elaborate process called the "glacial acetic acid extraction method." About four milligrams of growth hormone are derived from each gland.

The needs of children who are afflicted with pituitary dwarfism vary. Ten whose treatment has been completed each required, over the course of a five-year period, about 2,600 milligrams—an amount that called for the processing of 650 pituitaries.

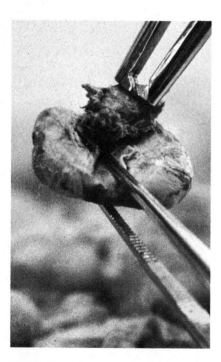

PREPARING THE RAW MATERIAL
Using tweezers, a technician *(right)* peels away the tough covering from human pituitaries *(close-up above)*, to prepare them for the process of extracting growth hormone. The dish in the foreground holds unpeeled glands covered with acetone to keep them damp. To obtain the hormone for patients, Dr. Raben's laboratory processes 30,000 pituitaries each year.

166

REFINING THE INGREDIENTS

Dried pituitaries, already chopped up in a blender, are spooned into a flour-grinding machine to be milled into an extremely fine powder. The powder finally yields up its precious growth hormone in the course of a complicated extraction and chemical purification procedure.

WEIGHING THE END PRODUCT

Dr. Raben, his brow furrowed in concentration, meticulously measures a supply of growth-hormone powder on a sensitive electric balance. Throughout the extraction process great care is exercised not to waste any of the hormone powder, which is more valuable than gold dust.

The Search for a New Source

ISOLATING THE HORMONE
An ordinary kitchen blender homogenizes pituitaries in a saline solution to milk-shake consistency, as a first step in determining the structure of HGH. Ice cools the mixture, and the small bottle contains sodium hydroxide, needed to control the degree of acidity of the mixture.

While Dr. Raben at Tufts is using human growth hormone in his treatment of dwarfed human beings, a research team on the West Coast is studying the hormone with the aim of deciphering its molecular structure. Once this has been done, chemists may be able to produce the substance artificially and thereby supplement the present limited supply. The man in charge of the study is Professor C. H. Li *(opposite)*, a tall, slim Chinese-American Lasker Award winner. It was Li's isolation of human growth hormone in 1956 that led to the new treatment for pituitary dwarfism. The job that Li and his associates have tackled is both formidable and tedious. The chainlike molecule of the growth-hormone protein is composed of no less than 187 different amino-acid residues. Every one of these acids must be identified and placed in its precise position in the chain. The researchers hope, however, that they may not need to discover the complete structure in order to produce medically useful growth hormone. Working with another hormone, Professor Li has found that part of the chain is just as active as the whole. Growth hormone may prove effective in treating other ailments besides dwarfism. Experiments with animals suggest that it may one day help to heal burns and knit broken bones.

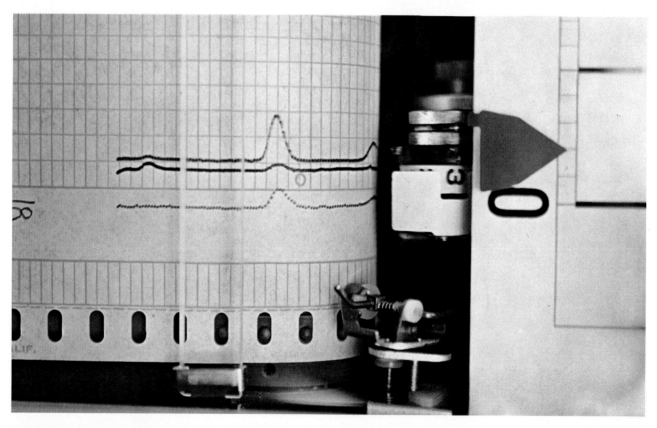

ANALYZING THE COMPONENTS
The amino-acid residues contained in a sample of growth hormone reveal their presence in a series of blips recorded on the graph paper of an automatic analyzer. The order, position and shape of the peaks tell which acids are present and in what quantities. The automatic analyzer is not only faster but also more accurate than conventional test-tube methods of analysis.

PIECING THE STRUCTURE TOGETHER
Writing on a sheet of Plexiglas, Professor Li discusses part of the molecular structure of human growth hormone with his team at the Hormone Research Laboratory at the University of California at Berkeley. Putting together the amino-acid residues in proper order resembles the process of "breaking" a complicated code.

8
"Tampering" with Nature

FOR CENTURIES biologists studied growth by patient observation. Now they are finding ways of improving and controlling growth that would have seemed fantastic a generation ago. Current investigations suggest that the future may bring methods of improving the quality of livestock that will make selective breeding seem clumsy and primitive; substances that suspend the aging process and prolong youth; "test-tube babies" grown from embryo to birth in the laboratory.

All of these investigations involve experiments that tamper with nature. Normally, human beings cannot be used as subjects of biological experiments, and so the experimenter must find or develop a sort of human proxy—an animal similar to man, and one which can be raised in the laboratory. This is what Dr. Gertrude van Wagenen, of the Department of Obstetrics and Gynecology of Yale University, set out to do in 1931, when she bought a rhesus monkey at a pet store in New Haven. Best known as the experimental animal used in the discovery of the Rh factor in human blood, the rhesus—which is also known as the macaque—makes a fine proxy for the study of human growth. Like all monkeys, it closely resembles man in physical structure. The female rhesus has a menstrual cycle of 28 days, exactly that of a human female. Because it has a gestation period of six months and reaches physical maturity in only three years, the rhesus makes it possible to carry on breeding experiments over many generations in a comparatively short span of time. Over the years, Dr. van Wagenen increased her stock. By 1955 there had been 354 pregnancies and three sets of twins, and the monkeys had become a local institution—the "Yale Obstetrical Colony." The Colony's infants are weighed every day and measured every week; monkeys more than a year old are weighed and measured monthly. Nearly a hundred monkeys have been followed, in thousands of measurements and X-rays, to the age of seven, equal to 20 years in humans. It was only after this painstaking work, which set the standards of normal growth and development for the monkey Colony, that experimentation could begin.

Some of the first experiments concerned the process of maturation. Students of human growth have long known that the androgens, the male hormones produced both in the testes and the adrenal glands, promote maturity in the human male. Dr. van Wagenen proved that the same was true of monkeys. Treated with the androgen testosterone, young males grew at twice the normal rate and matured 12 months earlier than usual. Then Dr. van Wagenen treated young female monkeys with the hormone and got some curious results. Like the males, they matured faster; they had their first menstruations at half the normal age, and by that time had reached the size of normal pubertal monkeys. At this point, the treatment was stopped. The monkeys continued to develop normally in every respect, even bearing infants.

THE NEED FOR MOTHER LOVE
In a University of Wisconsin experiment exploring emotional needs of the young, a psychologist carefully watches the behavior of a baby monkey clinging to its mother, an emotionally disturbed animal that often ignores or strikes her child. When offered the terry-cloth substitute mother, seen here outside the cage, the baby monkey will still choose its real mother.

The Yale experiment may already have thrown new light on the process of maturation in the human female. Androgens are far more powerful agents of growth and development than the corresponding female hormones, the estrogens. Although the estrogens are known to stimulate the onset of puberty in girls, these experiments suggest that they may not be the sole agents. The adrenal glands of females normally secrete small amounts of androgens which produce the changes in height and weight that accompany the adolescent growth spurt. Perhaps they also help trigger a young girl's step into womanhood.

Physically sound, emotionally upset

Dr. van Wagenen has used the Yale Obstetrical Colony to explore physical problems of growth. At the University of Wisconsin, another monkey colony serves as an experimental population for the study of psychological development. At Yale, Dr. van Wagenen had found that infant monkeys raised on the bottle had a lower mortality rate than infants nursed by their mothers. At Wisconsin, Dr. Harry F. Harlow and his colleagues, setting out to build a monkey colony of their own, followed Dr. van Wagenen's example. They separated newborn infants from their mothers, bottle-fed them, and raised them in separate cages. The monkeys grew up healthy and strong, but Dr. Harlow soon realized that they were emotionally disturbed. They would "sit in their cages and stare fixedly into space, circle their cages in a repetitive manner, clasp their heads in their hands and arms for long periods of time. . . . Often the approach of a human being [became] the stimulus for self-aggression. . . ."

Suspecting that this abnormal behavior might be caused simply by a lack of "mothering," Dr. Harlow supplied the baby monkeys with "surrogate mothers": wire frames covered with terry cloth and topped by crudely fashioned monkey heads. All the infants formed deep attachments to their "mothers," huddling against them most of the day and clinging to them for reassurance whenever a new object was introduced into the cage. As infants, these monkeys appeared stable and psychologically healthy. But as adults, they were nearly as withdrawn and anti-social as the motherless monkeys, and they would not mate.

The researchers then tried a new experiment. They raised one group of monkeys with natural mothers and a second group with terry-cloth mothers, but brought the two groups of infants together for some part of every day. At first the mothered group was more active and seemed to be growing more normally. Then the second group began to catch up. By the time the animals were two years old the differences between them had completely disappeared. And when they became adults, the members of the second group were as normal in their social and sexual life as those of the first.

Harlow's experiments have led him to suspect a basic pattern of psy-chological development in monkeys. During the first months of its life, an infant monkey depends completely upon its mother. About the third or fourth month, when the mother normally begins to reject her child from time to time, an infant-infant relationship assumes considerable importance. In fact, some of the experiments at Wisconsin seem to show that the relationships between the monkey infants can eventually compensate for a lack of mothering.

Where Van Wagenen and Harlow experimented with the chemistry and environment of their experimental animals after birth, other scientists have worked with animals before birth, studying the mechanisms of growth and heredity in order to discover the extent to which the egg is influenced by its uterine environment and the extent to which its development is predetermined by heredity. At the Institute of Animal Genetics in Edinburgh, Scotland, Anne McLaren mated mice with five vertebrae in their spines with others whose spines had six vertebrae. Some of the mothers were of the five-bone strain, while others were of the six-bone strain. If heredity alone had determined the characteristics of the offspring, half of them would have had five bones and the other half six. But more than heredity was at work: the majority of animals in each litter had the same number of vertebrae as their mothers. Moreover, when Dr. McLaren took hybrid fetuses from the wombs of six-bone mothers and implanted them in females with five bones, most of the offspring resembled their foster mothers rather than their biological mothers. Apparently, the uterine environment exerts an enormous influence on some aspects of physical growth.

Sheep airlifted in rabbits

In 1960, scientists in Cambridge, England, transplanted eight fertilized eggs from the uterus of a pedigreed sheep to the uterus of a rabbit. Thereafter, the rabbit was flown to South Africa, where it arrived four days after the transplanting operation. The eggs were immediately removed and each one was transplanted into the uterus of a nonpedigreed sheep. In six cases, the transplant did not take. However, in due course the other two sheep bore fine pedigreed lambs. This was not a stunt. It costs less to send a rabbit to South Africa than a lamb. Also, the rabbit did not have to spend time in quarantine in South Africa, whereas a lamb might have had to spend as much as three months.

Normally, a sheep or cow produces five to 10 offspring during its life-time. On the other hand, if it is treated with a pituitary hormone it can be made to produce hundreds of fertile eggs in this same period. It is for this reason that the new knowledge of transplanting techniques may become a practical tool. Suppose that an animal of high genetic quality is stimulated to produce hundreds of eggs. Transplanters could switch these eggs to the wombs of females of inferior quality, there to grow and be born as pedigreed stock. The technique would speed up the slow, uncertain process of selective breeding.

Survival outside the mother

Mouse and rabbit eggs can survive outside the body for about three days. During this time they develop into the ball of cells called a blastocyst, which normally implants itself in the wall of the uterus. Implantation is still possible; inserted into a living uterus, the blastocyst can still develop normally to birth.

Biologists are now working on the creation of an artificial womb to take the place of the natural one. Qualified investigators believe that success is only a matter of time.

Another rewarding field of research in growth is in regeneration, a faculty in which lower animals outdo man by far. Some lower animals are nearly indestructible: the hydra, for instance, can be chopped into several pieces, each of which will then grow into a complete organism. Even higher animals and man show traces of regenerative powers. A broken bone knits and, in a child, begins to grow again. Skin grows over a wound (if the damaged area is not too large), and the muscles and connective tissues beneath repair themselves.

Scientists had learned much about the "how" of regeneration before they began to understand the "why." Watching a salamander regenerate a limb, they saw that the process begins when the skin heals over the cut end of the limb. Beneath the new skin undifferentiated cells appear, multiplying with almost cancerlike freedom. Soon this growth slows down. Within 10 days the bud of a new limb can be seen, closely resembling the normal limb bud of a growing fetus. By the third or fourth week the beginnings of an elbow and a hand or foot are visible. Inside the new limb, the undifferentiated cells are specializing into muscle, tendon and bone. About a week later, fingers or toes appear, and the limb becomes functional.

This description, accurate as far as it goes, leaves all the important questions unanswered. What signal or trigger starts a new process of growth to replace a missing limb or organ? Why do many lower animals have so much regenerative power, and higher animals so little? And why do some animals lose the power to regenerate as they grow older? Young tadpoles, for instance, can quickly regenerate a lost limb, but adult frogs cannot. Could regenerative power be restored to a frog?

Though few knew it at the time, the first of these problems—the identification of the regenerative trigger—was partially solved more than a

A STUDY IN REGENERATION by embryologist Paul Weiss in 1925 showed that a limb must regenerate outward from the point of loss. In the experiment, diagrammed here, the humerus bone of a salamander's foreleg *(left, color)* was first removed surgically. After the wound healed, Weiss amputated the limb through the region of the missing bone *(center)*. Convincing evidence of one-way regrowth was provided when the lost limb grew back without any new bone appearing in back of the cut *(right)*.

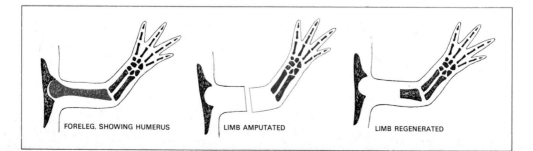

FORELEG, SHOWING HUMERUS   LIMB AMPUTATED   LIMB REGENERATED

century ago. In 1823, an English investigator named Tweedy Todd amputated a salamander's leg, then cut the nerve running to the stump. The limb did not regenerate. Long after Todd's death, 20th Century scientists confirmed his strange discovery. Somehow, the nerve at the site of a regenerating part is necessary to the process. If the nerve is cut, regeneration will not begin; if it is cut after regeneration has begun, growth ceases. The nerve need not even be cut: a nerve-paralyzing drug will stop regeneration as effectively as surgery. In short, anything that stops the continuous action of the nerve seems to stop regeneration.

It was Marcus Singer of Cornell University who moved on to investigate the next great problem of regeneration: why do such animals as tadpoles lose regenerative power as they grow older, and why do higher animals have so little of it? Perhaps, reasoned Singer, it is the number of nerve fibers, as compared with other kinds of tissue, that decides whether regeneration will take place. At Princeton University, J. M. van Stone showed that as a tadpole matures, the ratio of its nerve fibers to the cells of other tissues steadily decreases. Singer devised an experiment which reversed this process. He amputated the front leg of an adult frog and dissected out the large sciatic nerve of the frog's rear leg, leaving only the root attached. By careful manipulation, he pulled the nerve through the frog's body to the stump of the amputated leg. If Singer's theory was sound, the number of nerve fibers at the site now exceeded some unknown critical number—the number needed to start regeneration. And in the next three months the frog did indeed grow a new leg—deformed but recognizable. Man had restored regenerative power to an animal.

The wonders of metamorphosis

A tadpole loses its regenerative power as it turns into a frog, but it also gains new powers—the ability to breathe air is but one example. In addition, it changes its form as it grows. This transformation, called metamorphosis, is not uncommon in the animal kingdom. A butterfly shifts through a bewildering variety of forms: from an egg to a worm-like caterpillar to a closely wrapped, dormant chrysalis and finally—by metamorphosis—to the brilliant adult insect. Metamorphic growth, surely the most dramatic style of growth in nature, has begun to provide insights into the nature of all animal growth. When a tadpole turns into a frog, its tail gradually vanishes; in the language of biology, the tail is "resorbed." The tail steadily "ungrows." Finally, a mere stub, it falls off.

The cells of the shrinking tail seem literally to be destroying themselves in a sort of mass cellular suicide. Many—perhaps all—animal cells contain the microscopic particles that galvanize this process. Scientists have known of their existence since 1949, but it was not until 1955 that

Christian de Duve and Alex B. Novikoff, working at Albert Einstein College of Medicine in New York City, saw them under the electron microscope and identified them as minute bags of powerful digestive fluid. De Duve and Novikoff gave the tiny bodies a new name, lysosomes—or, more graphically, "suicide bags." Like the poison which a spy conceals to kill himself under the threats of torture, lysosomes wait in readiness to kill the cell that contains them. No one knows what triggers a lysosome to do its deadly work, but living bodies must, at one time or another, get rid of some of their cells. Indeed, "ungrowing" is often as important to development as growth itself. In higher animals, lysosomes may play a part in the process that accompanies all growth and at last puts an end to growth—the process of aging.

A hormone to prolong youth

The British zoologist V. B. Wigglesworth, who has spent a lifetime studying metamorphosis, has discovered a substance that may be connected with the nature of youth, just as lysosomes seem to be related to the process of aging. Working with the bloodsucking insect *Rhodnius*, Dr. Wigglesworth found that when he cut the head from a larva the body soon metamorphosed into an adult. He reasoned that the head must contain some inhibiting substance which kept the insect in the larval state. Careful dissection revealed two tiny glands in the larva's head. It is these glands that secrete the substance, called the juvenile hormone, that Dr. Wigglesworth was looking for. When the larva reaches a certain size, the glands stop secreting and the insect metamorphoses. If the glands of a young larva are implanted into an old one, metamorphosis is postponed. The old larva continues to grow until at last its new glands stop secreting. Then, when it finally does metamorphose, it becomes a giant insect.

Dr. Wigglesworth's discovery may explain why, during the earth's Carboniferous period, about 200 million years ago, there were insects with three-foot wing spans. The glands of these insects may have gone on secreting the juvenile hormone far longer than is the case now.

The unexplained power of the juvenile hormone to arrest metamorphosis has led to a new search for a substance that will prolong youth and growth in man. The possibility is remote, but scientists do not dismiss it lightly, and hardheaded cosmetics manufacturers have already begun to talk about this "Peter Pan hormone."

At every stage of growth—in age, in youth, in the period of gestation before birth—new windows of research and discovery are being opened. But even before growth begins, certain irrevocable "growth decisions" have been made, decisions that go into effect at the moment of conception. Can man tamper with these basic decisions, which affect the course of growth from conception to death? One scientist, Dr. Landrum B.

THE DISCOVERY OF SPERMATOZOA, though credited to the 17th Century Dutch microscopist Anton van Leeuwenhoek, actually was made by one of his students, who pointed out the male reproductive cells to him. Leeuwenhoek made accurate drawings *(above)* of what he saw through his homemade lenses. The larger pair above is from a dog, while the smaller came from a rabbit. In each pair, the left-hand sperm is living and mobile.

Shettles of Columbia University, College of Physicians and Surgeons, thinks he has found a way to do so. Dr. Shettles' theories are still highly controversial, but if they are proved sound, parents of the future will be able to choose the sex of their children.

It is the sperm that determines the sex of a child. Sperm carrying a Y chromosome give rise to male offspring, while sperm carrying an X chromosome give rise to females. From the time he was a medical student at Johns Hopkins University, Dr. Shettles carried out thousands of microscopic examinations of sperm cells, searching in vain for a clear difference between these two types of sperm. Eventually he turned to the phase-contrast microscope, a relatively new instrument which shows far more detail in living material than a conventional microscope. Almost at once, he says, the difference "just jumped out" at him. In a study of hundreds of normal men, he found two distinct populations of sperm cells —one with small, round heads, the other with larger, more oval heads. From the size and shape of the chromosomes within the sperm cells, Shettles guessed that the smaller cells carried Y chromosomes and the larger ones X chromosomes.

Now he had a working hypothesis: the small sperm cells were the male-producing ones, the larger ones, female. But it was—and still is—no more than a hypothesis. Scientists generally agree that sperm cells come in two distinct sizes and shapes, but there is little agreement as yet that this fact has anything to do with sex determination.

To confirm his hypothesis, Shettles has been accumulating evidence from statistical studies and laboratory experiments. He began by studying families in which mainly male children have been born for generations. In one such family, in Ohio, only male children were born over a period of 120 years; another, in England, had 33 males and two females in 256 years. Shettles examined sperm specimens from the men of such families, and found that small sperm cells outnumbered the larger ones by as much as 24 to 1. Examination of sperm cells from 500 men, selected at random, showed that the small cells still outnumbered the larger ones—but only by about 2 to 1. And it is known that more males are conceived than females. Though not conclusive, such statistics buttress Dr. Shettles' argument that the small cells are indeed the "male" ones.

Speedy "males" and long-lived "females"

The experimental work is even more encouraging. Studying his two sperm populations, Shettles has found that the "male" and "female" cells differ in ways other than size and shape. The small "male" cell swims more rapidly than the "female" one; it has a shorter life; and, as might be expected, it is lighter in weight. Taken together, the first two of these facts may help to explain how the decision between male and female is

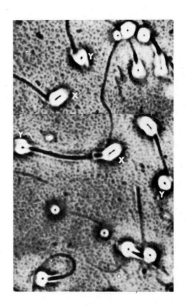

DETERMINATION OF SEX—by the female egg or the male sperm—was long the subject of controversy. Then experiments early in the 20th Century proved that the male produces two types of chromosome-containing sperm—an X type and a Y type—either of which combines with the egg and decides the sex of the child. Recent photomicrographs by Landrum B. Shettles (above) suggest that the female-forming sperm might be those with oval heads and a dark line that probably represents the X chromosome. The round head of the presumed male-forming sperm contains a dot which is probably the smaller Y chromosome.

made at conception. If intercourse occurs after the egg has been shed and is ready for fertilization, the fast-swimming "male" sperm cell will probably reach the egg first and therefore a male is more likely to be conceived. If intercourse occurs before the shedding of the egg, most of the short-lived "male" cells may die off, leaving a majority of slow but long-lived "female" ones.

In artificial-insemination experiments on cattle, other investigators have already controlled the sex ratios of offspring to a degree that cannot be explained by chance alone. Experiments are now under way based on the difference in weight between the two types of sperm cells. These may be crucial tests of Shettles' theory. In a centrifuge, a laboratory instrument which works on the same principle as the cream separator, "male" and "female" sperm cells might be separated from one another. The heavier "female" cells would be thrown by centrifugal force to the bottom of a test tube; the lighter "male" ones would remain at the top. In effect, science would be isolating two types of semen that are normally found together: one type that could produce only male offspring, and a second type that could produce only female. By using one or the other as a medium of artificial insemination, parents could decide for themselves whether to have a boy or a girl, and an age-old dream of mankind would be attained.

Determination of Size and Shape

The way a man grows, the size and shape he becomes, are determined by the complex and often obscure interaction of two agents, heredity and environment. Everyone inherits from his parents a genetic blueprint that specifies what kind of physique he will have, how much his bones will grow, what color his eyes will be. And then his environment, in the form of climate, diet or disease, works on these genetic possibilities, encouraging some, inhibiting others. Sometimes heredity and environment collaborate over long periods of time to develop a particular characteristic, such as great height. Sometimes a harmful environmental factor like malnutrition acts directly to disrupt normal growth patterns. Man can govern his own growth to some extent by controlling his diet and health. But there are so many variables at work that though some generalizations can be made, it is quite impossible to predict exactly how any individual will grow.

THE TALL, THIN DINKA

The man shown leaning gracefully on his spear on the opposite page is a member of the Dinka tribe, one of several Nilotic tribes in tropical Africa. They represent a genetic adaptation to the demands of environment: almost without exception the Nilotics grow to be extraordinarily tall and thin. This is a specialized physique that helps them live successfully in their very hot climate.

PART-TIME HOMES

In spite of their size, the Dinkas live in these small huts on the banks of the Nile. The houses are temporary, since each year's floods wash them away and chase the Dinkas to drier land.

HEAD AND SHOULDERS HIGHER

A Shilluk from south Sudan stands out in a market crowd of north Sudanese. The Shilluks, like other Nilotic tribesmen, have more or less normal torsos with disproportionately long legs. They intrigue visitors with their habit of standing for hours, crane-fashion, on one foot.

Shaped by a Harsh Land

In the blistering Nile Basin of southern Sudan live the Nilotic tribes, the world's tallest people. Their extraordinary height, in some tribes averaging close to six feet, is a clear example of the interaction of heredity and environment on human growth. The climate in southern Sudan is so fiercely hot and humid—summer temperatures average 108°F.—that humans of normal stature would be very uncomfortable living there. Centuries of genetic adaptation have provided the Nilotics with their particularly tall, thin physique that allows the body to dissipate more heat through greater surface areas than it could with any other shape.

The isolation of these tribes, whose members almost never interbreed with shorter peoples, has helped to establish their hereditary trend toward extreme height. The results of generations of genetic purity are particularly noticeable in two of the most isolated Nilotic tribes, the Dinkas and Shilluks, shown on these pages.

A DANCE AND A DIET
Four lanky Dinka boys do a ritual ox dance, holding sticks to represent horns of oxen, which are the Dinkas' most prized possession. Cattle-herding is the boys' chief occupation and the animals are the source of a high-protein milk and meat diet that helps keep the Dinkas so thin.

181

PYGMIES IN NEW GUINEA

Territorial Officer Allan Johnston towers over three diminutive New Guineans, none taller than four and a half feet. About 13,000 of these Pygmies live, isolated in one valley, in New Guinea. Slightly taller than the African Pygmies on the opposite page, they are also considerably more muscular and athletic. Their broad faces have Asiatic rather than Negroid features.

The Pygmy Mystery

In isolated parts of Africa, India and Melanesia live groups of people, unrelated to one another, who never grow taller than four and a half feet. Unlike the lanky physique of the Nilotics, which is a clear case of genetic and environmental interaction, the Pygmies' diminutive stature is hard to explain. Some anthropologists feel the Pygmy may represent an early model of *Homo sapiens* that has managed to survive. Another theory holds that the shortness resulted from chance mutations preserved by centuries of inbreeding. However it came about, the Pygmies' small size is by now firmly programmed into their genetic makeup. As long as they continue their present isolated existence, they will probably remain that way.

HOME OF LILLIPUTIANS
African Pygmy women use pestles to prepare food in their Congo village. Though smaller than New Guinea Pygmies, the Africans are nevertheless very strong. Men win their hunting spurs by killing an elephant single-handed, running underneath it and piercing it with a spear.

A VISIT TO THE OUTSIDE
Two four-foot-four-inch Pygmies are measured for clothes by a five-foot-eight-inch tailor in a village near the Pygmies' jungle home. Pygmies often visit their neighbors, and their women sometimes marry into other tribes, but Pygmy men very rarely take wives from the outside.

183

DARRELL CHAMBERS 5' 10"

LEROY BUCKINGHAM 5' 9"   ④ LARRY BUCKINGHAM 5' 6"   ⑤ VICKI LYNN CHAMBERS   MAXINE EZELL BEATTY 5' 6"   ④ KIRK BEATTY 6' 0"

③ JANELL BEATTY BUCKINGHAM 5' 0"   ④ SHARON BUCKINGHAM CHAMBERS 4' 11"   ③ NEWELL BEATTY 5' 8½"   ④ TERRY BEATT

FOUNDERS OF A FAMILY

Alba and Mack Beatty, at right *(and right center in group picture above)*, had two sons and three daughters whose average height (5'4") comes close to their parents' average (5'3").

IN BETWEEN

Larry Buckingham, 5'6" *(far right)*, is between his parents' heights (5'9" and 5'0") but nearer that of his father, as boys are apt to be. Girls average nearer the heights of their mothers.

HIGHER THAN BOTH

Six-footer Kirk Beatty *(far right)* is taller than both his parents. In a statistical average of a mass of people, his extra height would be balanced by someone shorter than both parents.

184

① MARY WRIGHT 5' 2"		④ LAURA FORNEY		④ MARCIA McCRACKEN		④ BRENDA McCRACKEN
DORIS KAVANAUGH BEATTY 5' 2"	② MACK BEATTY 5' 8"	④ CYNTHIA FORNEY	④ DENIS FORNEY	ROBERT McCRACKEN 6' 1½"	④ MELODY McCRACKEN	
HOWARD BEATTY 5' 7"	② ALBA WRIGHT BEATTY 4' 10"	RUSSELL FORNEY 5' 7"	③ NORMA BEATTY FORNEY 5' 2"		③ MARLINE BEATTY McCRACKEN 5' 1½"	

THE GATHERED CLAN

The large family gathering shown above during a reunion at Garden Grove, California, in 1965 was headed by 83-year-old Mrs. Mary Wright, and included one great-great-granddaughter. Circled numbers indicate family generations.

The Difficulty of Predicting

Geneticists know that in a whole nation of people the overall height of all offspring will be just halfway between their parents' heights. In the five-generation family shown above, there are some grown children who conform to this pattern. But there are many who do not (*opposite*), because the rule is based on statistical analysis of a great number of people. It cannot be applied to an individual, whose growth is subject to innumerable unforeseeable influences of heredity and environment. The fact is that no one can ever be sure how tall any one person will turn out to be.

NEW PROSPECTS FOR HEIGHT

Darrell Chambers (5'10") and Robert McCracken (6'1½"), who married into the Beatty family, are considerably taller than most of their male in-laws. The average adult height of the Beatty family is still well below the American average, but continued intermarriage with such tall types as Chambers and McCracken will almost certainly boost the height of future generations.

Mankind on the Way Up

The past several centuries have witnessed pronounced increases in the height of populations all around the world. For example, most modern soldiers *(right)* would have a hard time fitting into medieval armor. Houses built in New England 300 years ago seem quaint today because of the diminutive size of everything, particularly the height of doorways. In 1920 the average student at Harvard University was one and a quarter inches taller and 10 pounds heavier than the average student had been a generation earlier.

Scientists still have not pinpointed the exact cause of this accelerated growth. Environmental changes such as improvements in public health, nutrition and child care are unquestionably responsible to some degree, but there seem to be genetic factors at work, too. For instance, industrialization and increases in the size of human beings seem to go hand in hand. Industrial expansion takes relatively inbred country people and transports them to cities, where they intermarry. Apparently the mixing of genetic stocks tends to produce bigger children. A full explanation of the long-term trend to greater height, however, will undoubtedly disclose other factors that are still unknown.

HEIGHT ON THE RISE
The height of the average Englishman between the 11th and 14th Centuries is estimated from careful measurements taken of bones exhumed from several graveyards in Great Britain. The American soldiers' heights are based on the medical records of millions of Army inductees.

MEDIEVAL ENGLISHMAN:
5' 6"

WORLD WAR I U.S. SOLDIER:
5' 7³/₄"

WORLD WAR II U.S. SOLDIER:
5' 8¹/₂"

U.S. SOLDIER AFTER 1958:
5' 8⁹/₁₀"

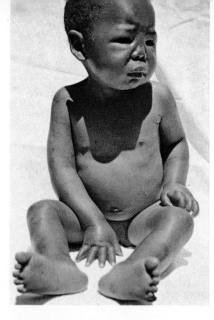

Stunted by Starvation

Only in recent decades have scientists discovered how seriously a bad diet can cripple the genetic possibilities for human growth. Millions of people, even whole races, are shorter than they might be or are malformed in other ways because chronic malnutrition (not necessarily starvation) in their early years has kept them from ever reaching their full genetic growth potential.

The most widespread nutritional disease is protein deficiency, known by the Ghanaian name of kwashiorkor. It afflicts children who do not get enough meat, fish, dairy products or vegetables of the proper kind. This deficiency inhibits growth, not only of bone and muscle, but also of hair, pigment cells and even the brain. Its most pernicious form is found in infants whose diet is suddenly switched from their mothers' milk to a starchy staple such as millet, rice or sweet potatoes. If this debilitating menu is improved in the early years, the child will respond by growing more quickly to catch up somewhat with his growth schedule. But if he remains protein-starved until the age of five, the damage is irreparable, and his genetic expectations will never be realized.

WAY BEHIND SCHEDULE
Elizabeth Zwane, an underdeveloped three-year-old girl from Johannesburg, South Africa, is a victim of kwashiorkor. Her skin is lighter than it should be, and her hair is too sparse. Most of these effects could still be cured by proper diet.

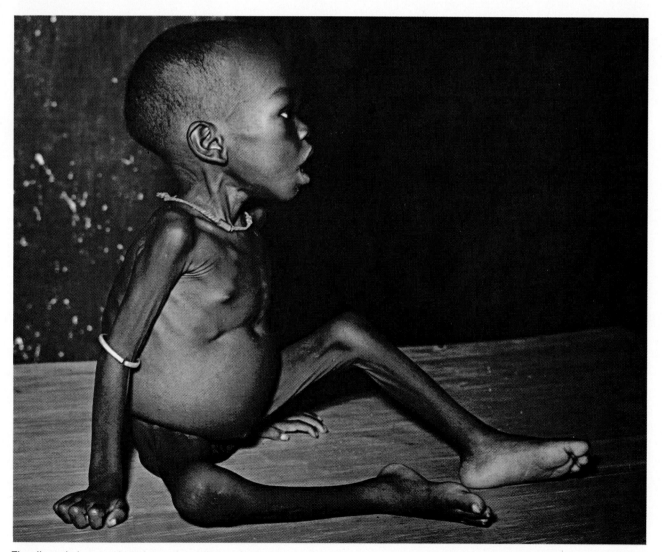

The distended stomach and emaciated limbs of this 18-month-old girl of Upper Volta in Africa are typical effects of kwashiorkor.

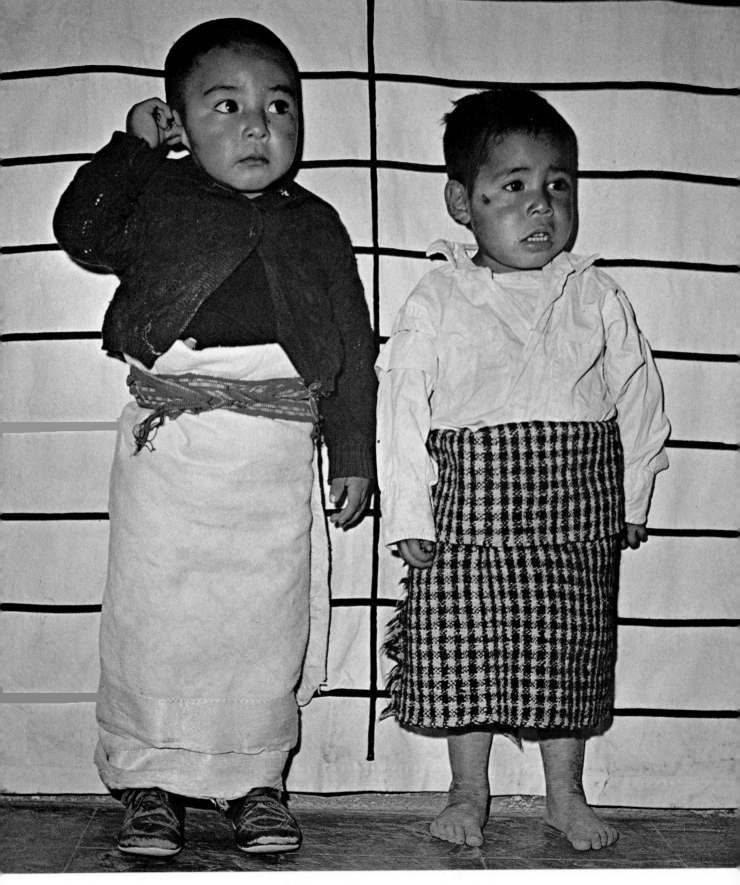

YOUNGER BUT TALLER

Two boys of the Guatemala highlands are proof that good diet improves growth in areas where malnutrition is endemic. The boy on the right, 42 months old, has been raised on the local starchy diet and is as tall as most children of his age in the area. The other boy, only 27 months old, has had his regular diet supplemented with a special protein-rich substance.

Super Size from Forced Feeding

AN ANCIENT RITUAL
Two sumo wrestlers of an earlier age are shown in this 18th Century print. The sport is about 1,200 years old and, like many aspects of the Japanese culture, it is a highly formalized ritual.

Japan's massive sumo wrestlers provide spectacular proof of the effect diet can have on a man's size—and shape. Sumo wrestling puts a great premium on bulk, since the contest is decided when one opponent gets bounced out of a ring. Genetics plays a part, too, because the wrestlers' shape and the squatting position they assume is possible only with the long torso common to the Japanese. Moreover, wrestlers are picked from among bigger-than-average youths.

But to achieve their optimum bulk of about 300 pounds, they must consume more than 5,000 calories a day in a special diet. They train something like football linemen, by shoving against pillars to develop their back and leg muscles. But exercise is restricted to short bouts each morning. There follows a huge noon meal, which mostly turns to bulk because the sumo wrestlers relax for the rest of the day.

The wrestlers pay a price for their ponderous prowess. They are highly vulnerable to diabetes, liver and kidney trouble, and die about 10 years earlier than the average Japanese.

A MONUMENTAL MEAL
Grand Champion Taiho, the most formidable sumo wrestler in Japan, eats as his lesser colleagues wait their turn. In the course of a typical lunch he literally stuffs himself with more than 10 pounds of rice and *chanko nabe*, a thick mulligan of chicken, fish and vegetables, and washes it down with beer. Supper is a light repast—he consumes only seven pounds of stew.

A MAN OF SUBSTANCE
Wakamiyama, who at 390 pounds is big even among sumo professionals, assumes the ritual squat before a match. Despite his ominous appearance, Wakamiyama's temperament is tranquil and childlike. His trainers protect him from disturbing problems that might cause worry and thereby possibly make him lose weight.

190

How a Human Face Takes Shape

The human face begins to be structured quite early in the womb. The process continues for a long time, until maturity. Two pits that will become the nasal passages are present by the fourth week. Beneath them are lobes that will join together to become the jaws. At five weeks rudimentary eyes have appeared on either side of the head, and the nose structure has moved below the facial midline. By the end of the second month the face already has a recognizable nose, complete upper and lower lips, cheeks and eyelids, and a basically human appearance. The ears, too, have started to form.

STEPS IN THE FASHIONING OF FEATURES

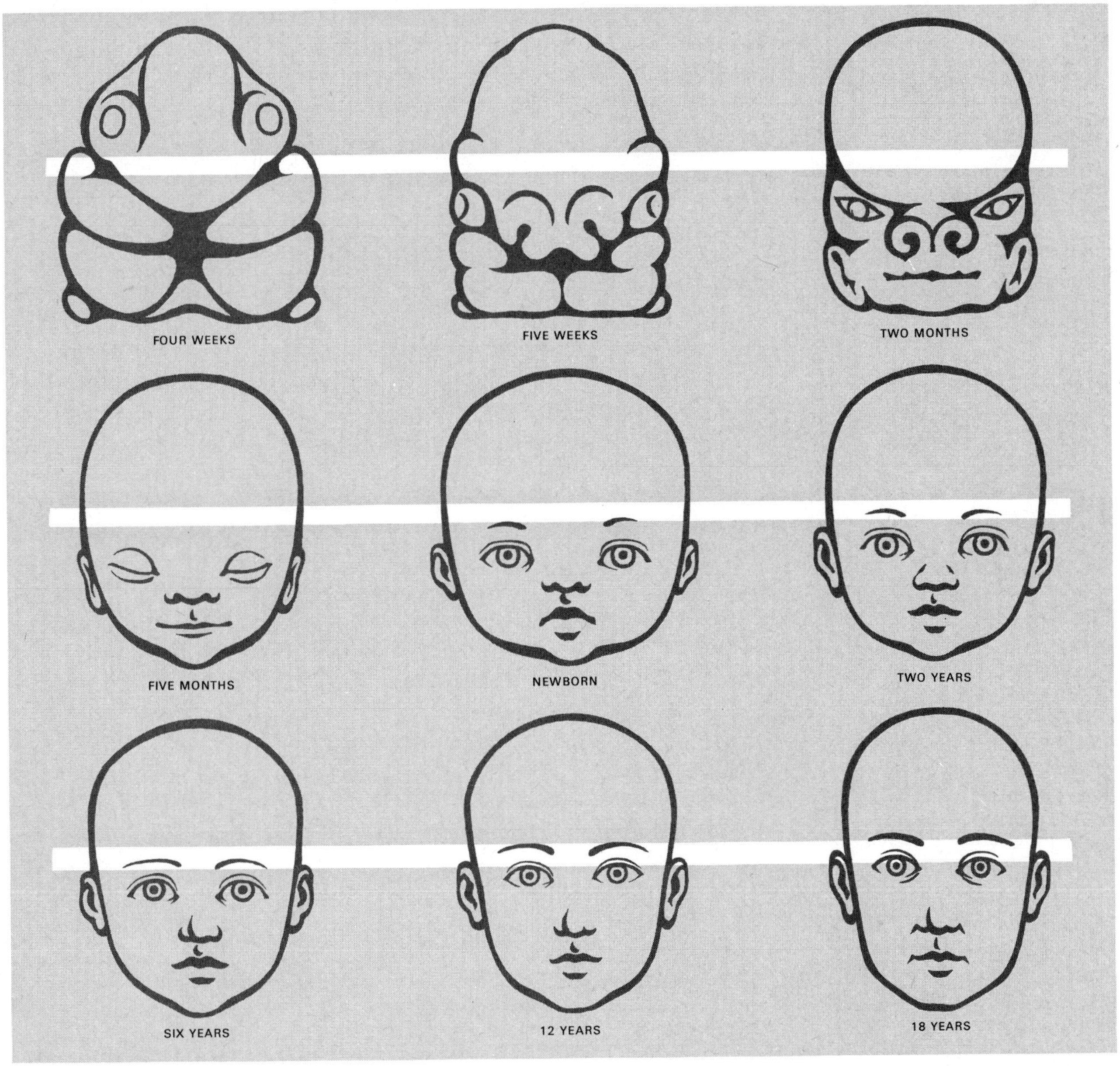

FOUR WEEKS

FIVE WEEKS

TWO MONTHS

FIVE MONTHS

NEWBORN

TWO YEARS

SIX YEARS

12 YEARS

18 YEARS

FROM FOUR WEEKS TO 18 YEARS

While most of the shaping of a face takes place within the womb, the facial proportions shift subtly between birth and adulthood. The eyes are already two thirds full size at birth and seem disproportionately large throughout childhood. Their growth is almost complete by age 12. The face becomes narrower during the years between childhood and adolescence as the jaw and chin rapidly lengthen and the "baby fat" disappears.

FURTHER READING

General

*Barth, Lucina Jaeger, *Development: Selected Topics.* Addison-Wesley, 1964.

*Bonner, John Tyler, *Morphogenesis.* Atheneum, 1963. *The Ideas of Biology.* Harper & Brothers, 1962.

Lehrman, Robert L., *The Reproduction of Life.* Basic Books, 1964.

Pfeiffer, John, and the Editors of LIFE, *The Cell.* Time Inc., 1964.

*Sussman, Maurice, *Growth and Development.* Prentice-Hall, 1964.

Taylor, Gordon Rattray, *The Science of Life.* McGraw-Hill, 1963.

Thompson, D'Arcy Wentworth, *On Growth and Form.* J. T. Bonner, ed. Cambridge University Press, 1961.

†Waddington, C. H., *How Animals Develop.* Harper & Row, 1962.

History of Embryology and Obstetrics

Findley, Palmer, *Priests of Lucina.* Little, Brown, 1939.

Graham, Harvey, *Eternal Eve.* Hutchinson, 1960.

Needham, Joseph, *A History of Embryology.* Abelard-Schuman, 1959.

Prenatal Development

Allan, Frank D., *Essentials of Human Embryology.* Oxford University Press, 1960.

*Ashley Montagu, M. F., *Life before Birth.* World Publishing, 1964.

Flanagan, Geraldine Lux, *The First Nine Months of Life.* Simon & Schuster, 1962.

*Guttmacher, Alan F., *Pregnancy and Birth.* Viking, 1962.

Hall, Robert E., *Nine Months' Reading.* Doubleday, 1960.

Patten, Bradley M., *Human Embryology.* McGraw-Hill, 1953.

Postnatal Development

Calverton, V. F., and S. D. Schmalhausen, eds., *Adolescence in Primitive and Modern Society in the New Generation.* Macauley, 1930.

†Crow, Lester D., and Alice, eds., *Readings in Child and Adolescent Psychology.* David McKay, 1961.

*Mead, Margaret, *Coming of Age in Samoa.* Peter Smith, 1962. *Growing Up in New Guinea.* Peter Smith, 1962.

Tanner, J. M., *Education and Physical Growth.* University of London Press, 1961.

Watson, E. H., and G. H. Lowrey, *Growth and Development of Children.* Yearbook Medical Publishers, 1962.

Control of Growth

*Asimov, Isaac, *The Genetic Code.* Orion Press, 1964.

†Brown, J.H.U., and S. B. Barker, *Basic Endocrinology.* F. A. Davis, 1962.

*Goldstein, Philip, *Genetics Is Easy.* Lantern Press, 1955.

Hutchins, Carleen Maley, *Life's Key: DNA.* Coward-McCann, 1961.

†Mason, A. Stuart, *Health and Hormones.* Penguin, 1961.

Macauley, 1930.

†Moore, John A., *Heredity and Development.* Oxford University Press, 1963.

*Riedman, Sarah R., *Our Hormones and How They Work.* Abelard-Schuman, 1956.

Scheinfeld, Amram, *Your Heredity and Environment.* J. B. Lippincott, 1965.

†Winchester, A. M., *Heredity and Your Life.* Dover, 1960.

Studies in Growth

Asimov, Isaac, *The Human Brain.* Houghton Mifflin, 1963.

Benda, Clemens E., *The Child with Mongolism.* Grune & Stratton, 1960.

*Ebert, James D., *Interacting Systems in Development.* Holt, Rinehart & Winston, 1965.

Fishbein, Morris, ed., *Birth Defects.* J. B. Lippincott, 1963.

Harrison, G. A., and others, *Human Biology.* Oxford University Press, 1964.

*Available in paperback edition.
†Available only in paperback edition.

ACKNOWLEDGMENTS

The editors of this book are especially indebted to Dr. Melvin M. Grumbach, Associate Professor of Pediatrics, Columbia University College of Physicians and Surgeons, New York City; and to the following persons and institutions: Dr. Alexander Bearn, Professor, The Rockefeller Institute, New York City; Dr. John Tyler Bonner, Department of Biology, Princeton University, Princeton, New Jersey; CARE Inc., New York City; Frank J. Darmstaeder, Curator, The Jewish Theological Seminary of America, New York City; Belle Fieldman, Thomas J. Watson Library, Metropolitan Museum of Art, New York City; Dr. Stanley M. Garn, Dr. John I. Lacey, Dr. Michael Lewis, Dr. Lester W. Sontag, Director, Fels Research Institute for the Study of Human Development, Yellow Springs, Ohio; Dr. Alan F. Guttmacher, Director, Planned Parenthood Federation of America, New York City; Institute of Nutrition of Central America and Panama (Guatemala); Dr. Stanley James, Babies Hospital, Columbia Presbyterian Medical Center, New York City; Dr. John H. Lawrence, Associate Director, Lawrence Radiation Laboratory, University of California at Berkeley; Dr. Choh Hao Li, The Hormone Research Laboratory, University of California at Berkeley; Margaret Mead, Associate Curator of Ethnology, American Museum of Natural History, New York City; National Academy of Sciences, National Research Council, Washington, D.C.; The National Pituitary Agency, 1900 McElderry Street, Baltimore 5, Maryland; Dr. Charles Noback, Professor of Anatomy, Columbia University College of Physicians and Surgeons, New York City; Dr. Paul R. Packer, Department of Obstetrics and Gynecology, Albert Einstein College of Medicine, New York City; Bradley M. Patten, Department of Anatomy, University of Michigan, Ann Arbor; Dr. Maurice S. Raben, Tufts New England Medical Center, Boston; Dr. John W. Saunders Jr., Chairman, Department of Biology, Marquette University, Milwaukee; Dr. Harry L. Shapiro, Chairman, Department of Anthropology, American Museum of Natural History, New York City; Dr. Landrum B. Shettles, Department of Obstetrics and Gynecology, Columbia University College of Physicians and Surgeons, New York City; Dr. Gertrude van Wagenen, Department of Obstetrics and Gynecology, Yale University School of Medicine, New Haven; Alice D. Weaver and librarians, Rare Book Department, New York Academy of Medicine; Dr. I. Bernard Weinstein, Assistant Professor of Medicine, Columbia University College of Physicians and Surgeons, New York City.

INDEX

Numerals in italics indicate a photograph or painting of the subject mentioned.

PICTURE CREDITS

Cover—Arnold Newman

CHAPTER 1: 8—Bill Ray. 11—Drawings by Leslie Martin. 12, 13—Henry Groskinsky courtesy The New York Academy of Medicine rare book room. 14, 15—Drawings by Otto van Eersel. 17, 18, 19—Drawings by Samuel Maitin. 20—Electron micrograph courtesy Dr. Bernard Tandler of Sloan-Kettering Institute for Cancer Research. 20 through 27—Drawings by Samuel Maitin.

CHAPTER 2: 28—Dr. Landrum B. Shettles courtesy *The American Journal of Obstetrics and Gynecology.* 30, 31—Adapted by Nicholas Fasciano from *Human Embryology* by Bradley M. Patten second edition copyright 1953. Blakiston Division, McGraw-Hill Inc.; used by permission. 32, 33, 34—Henry Groskinsky courtesy The New York Academy of Medicine rare book room. 35, 36, 37—Drawings by Nicholas Fasciano. 38, 39—Drawings by Eric Mose from an illustration in *Scientific American* November 1957. 41, 42, 43—Drawings by Samuel Maitin. 44, 45—Julius Weber except background and drawings by Samuel Maitin. 46—Drawing by Arnold Holeywell—courtesy Clay Adams Inc., New York City—drawings by Samuel Maitin (4). 47—Julius Weber. 48, 49—Professor Etienne Wolff (2), Professor A. A. Moscona (3)—drawing by Samuel Maitin adapted by permission from *Animal Growth and Development* by Maurice Sussman copyright 1960 Prentice-Hall. 50—Drawing by Samuel Maitin from an illustration in *Scientific American* November 1963. 51—Howard Sochurek—Dr. John W. Saunders Jr. 52—Ulrich Clever. 53—Claus Pelling courtesy Max Planck Institute for Biology.

CHAPTER 3: 54—Courtesy Bayer. Staatsbibliothek, München. 57—Drawings by Nicholas Fasciano. 59—Drawing by James Alexander. 60—Drawings adapted by Otto van Eersel from a drawing by Mrs. Audrey Besterman from *Science of Man 3* by permission of the British Broadcasting Corporation. 63 through 75—Lennart Nilsson.

CHAPTER 4: 76—Courtesy H. B. Osgood. 78—Drawings by Matt Greene. 80—Drawing by Nicholas Fasciano. 81—Drawing by Otto van Eersel. 87—Drawing by Patricia Byrne. 89, 90, 91—Burk Uzzle. 92, 93—Burk Uzzle—courtesy Fels Research Institute. 94 through 99—Burk Uzzle. 100, 101—Burk Uzzle, Bob Doty (2). 102, 103—Burk Uzzle.

CHAPTER 5: 104—Lisa Larsen. 107—A. Y. Owen courtesy The Oklahoma Historical Society. 108—Drawings by Otto van Eersel. 110, 111—Drawings by Matt Greene. 115—Henry Groskinsky. 116—Lilo Hess, Loomis Dean. 117—Andreas Feininger. 118, 119—Andreas Feininger, Douglas Faulkner—courtesy New York Public Library. 120, 121—Douglas Faulkner, Tom McHugh from Photo Researchers Inc.—Lawrence Chang. 122—Ivan Massar from Black Star (2)—courtesy New York Public Library. 123—Ivan Massar from Black Star except top right Gareth W. Coffin, U.S. Bureau of Commercial Fisheries Biological Laboratory, Boothbay Harbor, and the Maine Department of Sea and Shore Fisheries. 124—Tuggener-Foto, Zurich. 125—Marvin E. Newman. 126, 127—Left from *On Growth and Form* by Sir D'Arcy Thompson, abridged edition, published by Cambridge University Press; right Roy Pinney from Photo Library Inc. 128, 129—Carroll Seghers II, Myers from Alpha Photo Associates.

CHAPTER 6: 130—Phil Brodatz. 133—Drawing by Patricia Byrne courtesy Dr. Stanley M. Garn. 135—Courtesy The Royal College of Surgeons of England. 136—Drawing by Nicholas Fasciano. 139—Seymour Mednick. 140, 141—Drawings by Elliot Herman. 142 through 147—Drawings by Samuel Maitin. 148, 149—Drawing by Samuel Maitin, drawing by Elliot Herman.

CHAPTER 7: 150—Courtesy The Anna Clinic, Hannover. 152—Henry Groskinsky courtesy The New York Academy of Medicine rare book room. 153—Courtesy New York Public Library. 154—Adapted by Leslie Martin courtesy Clemens E. Benda: *The Child with Mongolism*, New York, Grune and Stratton 1960. 157—Phil Brodatz courtesy Watson Library, The Metropolitan Museum of Art. 159—London *Daily Mirror.* 160—Left Wide World; right from *The Pituitary Body and Its Disorders* by Harvey Cushing, published by J. B. Lippincott 1912. 161—Ted Streshinsky—Jon Brenneis. 162—Courtesy The Royal Canadian Air Force. 163—Left courtesy Anna Hooey; right drawing by Otto van Eersel. 164, 165—Horst Ehricht. 166, 167—Ivan Massar from Black Star. 168, 169—Jon Brenneis.

CHAPTER 8: 170—Dr. Robert Sponholtz. 174—Drawing by Leslie Martin from B. I. Balinsky, *An Introduction to Embryology*, published by W. B. Saunders Co. 176—Roy Hyrkin. 177—Dr. Landrum B. Shettles. 179—Dr. Lino Pellegrini. 180, 181—Tony Archer—R. Faust, Dr. Peter Fuchs, Göttingen. 182—Jens Bjerre. 183—Colin Turnbull courtesy Department of Anthropology, The American Museum of Natural History. 184, 185—J. R. Eyerman. 186, 187—Eric Schaal. 188—Dr. E. Kahn courtesy Harlem Hospital—Pierre A. Pittet. 189—I.N.C.A.P. 190—Courtesy Art Institute of Chicago; Frederick W. Gookin Trust Fund—T. Tanuma. 191—T. Tanuma. 193—Otto van Eersel based on drawing from CIBA *Symposia* page 1,469, formerly published by CIBA Pharmaceutical Company, Summit, N.J. Back Cover—Charles Mikolaycak.